# Grammar Rules!

High-Interest Activities for Practice and Mastery of Basic Grammar Skills

## Book 2

by Jillayne Prince Wallaker

# Dedication

With lots of love to Maegen, Madalen, Ian and always to Willie.

# Credits

**Editors:**
Tracy Soles, Donna Walkush

**Layout Design:**
Victory Productions, Inc.

**Illustrations:**
Janet Armbrust

**Cover Design:**
Peggy Jackson

First South Asian Edition, 2006
- 4262/3, Ansari Road, Daryaganj, New Delhi 110 002, E-mail: vivadelhi@viviagroupindia.net
- 215-216 New Apollo Estate, 2nd Floor, Mogra Lane, Andheri (E), Mumbai 400 069 E-mail: vivamumbai@viviagroupindia.net
- Jamal Fazal Chambers, 26 Greams Road, Chennai 600 006, E-mail: vivachennai@viviagroupindia.net
- B-103, Jindal Towers, 21/1A/3 Darga Road, Kolkata 700 017, E-mail: vivakolkata@viviagroupindia.net
- 7 Sovereign Park Appts., 56-58, K.R. Road, Basavanagudi, Bangalore 560 004 E-mail: vivabangalore@viviagroupindia.net
- 101-102 Moghal Marc Apartments, 3-4-637 to 641 First Floor, Narayanguda, Hyderabad 500 029 E-mail: vivahyderabad@viviagroupindia.net

*Published in arrangement with*

Published by Vinod Vasishtha for Viva Books Private Limited, 4262/3, Ansari Road, Daryaganj, New Delhi 110 002.

Printed and baund at Raj Press, R-3, Inderpuri, New Delhi 110 012

ISBN 81-309-0013-0

# Contents

# Contents

# Introduction

This grammar book was developed so that writing teachers can show students that grammar can be understood (and sometimes even fun) when presented in a clear, reasonable way. *Grammar Rules!* builds on each topic in a logical progression so that students learn the facts behind the skill, practise the skill, then are able to put their new grammar knowledge into action.

After each grammar skill is introduced, plenty of practice is provided, along with a Review Work and a Draft Book exercise for students to transfer their new skill. Review Work assignments focus on previously covered skills or provides additional practice with a skill on the given page. The Draft Book assignments encourage students to apply the grammar skills and incorporate them into their own writing. For the Draft Book activities, students can complete assignments on loose-leaf paper in a folder or in a spiral or composition notebook.

Each grammar skill presented in the Review Work and Draft Book exercises has a locator code, such as underlining nouns with yellow. This code is consistent throughout the book. This provides a student with a patterned tool for self-monitoring as well as self-editing.

This book also contains a comprehensive review on pages 112-113. These pages are perfect for a pre-lesson and post-lesson assessment or an end-of-year test.

A student editing checklist is included on pages 114-115. This page is designed to be used as a self-editing tool. By assigning two or three items to check at a time, students are not overwhelmed with "getting everything right", but instead can focus on very specific skills until they understand them completely. Once mastery of the selected editing skills is evident, an additional set of items can be assigned. The same piece of student writing can be used for several editing assignments or students can use different writing samples. This convenient checklist can be kept with each student Draft Book as a reminder of grammatical variations that can be included in their writing. It can also be used to monitor student progress by dating each skill when it is demonstrated consistently.

*Grammar Rules!* will quickly become a resource that writing teachers return to for strong grammar activities to show their students that grammar is really enjoyable!

Name ______________________________

# Categories

**nouns**

Nouns are words that name people, places, things or ideas.

**Write each noun in the correct category.**

| | | | |
|---|---|---|---|
| ocean | classmate | Megha | Neptune |
| carnival | computer | boredom | restaurant |
| peacock | imagination | mineral | happiness |
| pilot | parents | peace | South Asia |

| People | Places |
|---|---|
| ______________ | ______________ |
| ______________ | ______________ |
| ______________ | ______________ |
| ______________ | ______________ |
| ______________ | ______________ |

| Things | Ideas |
|---|---|
| ______________ | ______________ |
| ______________ | ______________ |
| ______________ | ______________ |
| ______________ | ______________ |
| ______________ | ______________ |
| ______________ | ______________ |

### Review Work

Write two nouns of your own in each category.

### Draft Book

Choose one noun from each category. Write one sentence with each noun. Underline each noun with yellow.

Name ________________________________

# Find the Nouns

**nouns**

Nouns are words that name people, places, things or ideas.

**Underline the nouns in the sentences.**

Chitra has a wonderful idea.

Kangaroos live in Australia.

Manas went to the course to play golf with his brother.

That turtle in the sink belongs to Anna.

The computer printed six pages of text.

Suman always encouraged Gaurav's creativity.

Irfan fertilised the plants by the window.

The boots in the hallway belong to Prem.

## Review Work

Write the nouns from the sentences in the correct categories.

People: ________________________________

________________________________

Places: ________________________________

________________________________

Things: ________________________________

________________________________

Ideas: ________________________________

________________________________

## Draft Book

Make lists of people you know, places you have been and things that interest you. These are all nouns! Include at least 10 nouns in each list. Use these nouns in future writing assignments.

Name ______________________________

# Names

## common and proper nouns

Common nouns are nouns that name unspecific or general people, places, things or ideas. Proper nouns are nouns that name specific people, places, things or ideas. A proper noun always starts with an uppercase letter. A person's first and last names are proper nouns. Titles like Mr., Mrs., Miss, Ms. and Dr. are proper nouns, too.

**examples:** girl, president, leader (common nouns)
**examples:** Aparna Sen, President Kalam, Nelson Mandela (proper nouns)

**Write each noun in the correct category. Capitalise the proper nouns.**

| | | | |
|---|---|---|---|
| neha | doctor | mr. preet | parent |
| teammate | nitya nair | dr. desai | gwalior |
| lalita | artist | student | cook |
| judge | howrah bridge | ram sharma | editor |

| **Common Nouns** | **Proper Nouns** |
|---|---|
| ______________________ | ______________________ |
| ______________________ | ______________________ |
| ______________________ | ______________________ |
| ______________________ | ______________________ |
| ______________________ | ______________________ |
| ______________________ | ______________________ |
| ______________________ | ______________________ |
| ______________________ | ______________________ |
| ______________________ | ______________________ |
| ______________________ | ______________________ |

### Review Work
Write two nouns of your own in each category.

### Draft Book
Write five sentences. Use a proper noun that names a person in each sentence.

Name ______________________________

# Pick and Fix

**proper nouns**

Proper nouns name specific people, places, things or ideas. A proper noun always starts with an uppercase letter.

**Circle the proper noun in each set of words. Rewrite it correctly.**

a house / the white house ______________________

qutab minar / a building ______________________

mr. billu / cat ______________________

nehru / a prime minister ______________________

mrs. srinivas / a woman ______________________

river / yamuna river ______________________

holiday / republic day ______________________

kerala / state ______________________

city / st. petersburg ______________________

sri lanka / island ______________________

my street / r p road ______________________

best friend / rahul sarkar ______________________

statue / statue of liberty ______________________

## Review Work

Write three common nouns on the top lines. Make them proper nouns on the lines below.

______________ ______________ ______________

______________ ______________ ______________

## Draft Book

Make a list of at least 10 proper nouns. You can include product names. Use these nouns in future writing assignments.

Name ____________________

# Common or Proper? proper nouns

Proper nouns name specific people, places, things or ideas. A proper noun always starts with an uppercase letter.

**Which nouns in the sentences are proper nouns? For each word that needs a beginning uppercase letter, cross out the lowercase letter and write the uppercase letter above it.**

The president of the company, ms. samant, is in her office.

gustave eiffel grew up in dijon, france. He designed the eiffel tower.

mr. kumar works for a company called build-it houses.

The red fort is in new delhi.

mount everest is located in the himalayan mountains.

tej went to bergerone, canada, to go whale watching.

jaidev, priya and mini will ride their bikes to goa beach.

jisha and paul are in a play called fireflies.

That picture shows a glacier separating in gangotri glacier, uttaranchal.

## Review Work

Underline the common nouns in the sentences with yellow.

## Draft Book

Write five sentences using common and proper nouns. Underline all of the nouns with yellow. Capitalise the proper nouns.

Name ______________________________

# Here and There

**proper nouns**

Proper nouns name specific people, places, things or ideas. A proper noun always starts with an uppercase letter. When proper nouns name a city and state, a comma goes between them.

**example:** Shimoga, Karnataka

**Write the names and addresses correctly. Capitalise the proper nouns. Put commas between the city and state names.**

mr. m. t. vasudevan ______________________

9210 mount road ______________________

chennai tamil nadu 600 002 ______________________

mrs. s. o. sachdev ______________________

215 apollo estate ______________________

mumbai maharashtra 400 049 ______________________

**For each proper noun that needs a beginning uppercase letter, cross out the lowercase letter and write the uppercase letter above it. Put commas between the city and state names.**

pragya and rohan's family plans to take a trip to jaipur rajasthan.

anant's grandmother lives in bhopal madhya pradesh.

ahmed stopped in agra uttar pradesh, on his way to delhi.

## Review Work

In the sentences, draw an X next to each proper noun that names a person. Draw a triangle above each proper noun that names a place.

## Draft Book

Write your name and address. Capitalise all of the proper nouns. Put a comma between the names of your city and state.

Name ______________________________

# Shorten It

**proper nouns**

Proper nouns name specific people, places, things or ideas. Some proper nouns can be abbreviated, or shortened. The complete words and their abbreviations always start with uppercase letters.

**example:** Rajiv C. Krishnan or R. C. K.
**example:** Mister Pradeep or Mr. Pradeep

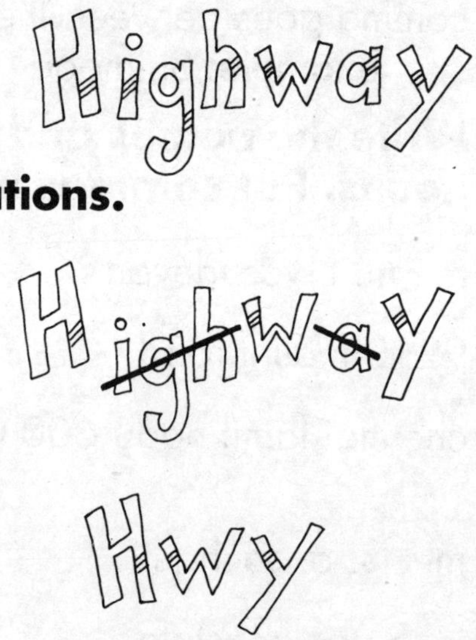


**Draw lines to match the nouns to their abbreviations.**

| | |
|---|---|
| company | Ave. |
| boulevard | Co. |
| street | Blvd. |
| avenue | USA |
| road | Dr. |
| United States of America | St. |
| doctor | Rd. |

## Review Work

Write your full name and a friend's full name. Write the initials after the names.

______________________________________________

______________________________________________

## Draft Book

Make a list of abbreviations. Add full stops to the abbreviations where they are needed. Write the complete words beside the abbreviations.

Name ______________________________

# Special Times

**proper nouns**

Days and months are proper nouns. Some of these nouns can be abbreviated. The complete words and their abbreviations always start with uppercase letters.

**Draw lines to match the nouns to their abbreviations.**

| | | | |
|---|---|---|---|
| Saturday | Tues. | Sunday | Apr. |
| February | Dec. | March | Nov. |
| Tuesday | Aug. | April | Wed. |
| August | Feb. | Wednesday | Sun. |
| Thursday | Thurs. | September | Oct. |
| Monday | Jan. | October | Mar. |
| December | Sat. | Friday | Sept. |
| January | Mon. | November | Fri. |

**Rewrite the sentences. Write the complete words instead of the abbreviations.**

Cindy goes to Vine St. for piano lessons every Mon., Wed. and Fri.

______________________________

______________________________

The coldest months in Jammu are Dec., Jan. and Feb.

______________________________

______________________________

## Review Work

Underline the nouns in the sentences with yellow.

## Draft Book

Write five sentences using nouns that name days and months. Write the abbreviations above the complete words.

Name ______________________________

# Make It Singular

**singular and plural nouns**

A noun can be singular (one person, place, thing or idea) or plural (more than one). Usually, a noun becomes plural by adding an *s* to the end. Sometimes, a noun becomes singular by removing the *s* from the end.

**Make the plural nouns singular. Use the nouns to finish the sentences. Decide if the plural or singular noun works best in each sentence.**

turtles ______________________________

Kavita found one painted ______________________________ .

Vinu found five box ______________________________ .

bears ______________________________

Shan saw three baby ______________________________

Vinay saw an angry ______________________________ .

ferrets ______________________________

Pooja owns a brown ______________________________ .

The pet store has many ______________________________ .

lizards ______________________________

Ayan caught that ______________________________ in a tree.

He tried to catch other ______________________________, but they ran away.

**Which words helped you decide whether you needed a singular or plural noun in each sentence? Circle the words that helped you. The first one has been done for you.**

## Review Work

Underline the other nouns in the sentences with yellow.

## Draft Book

Write a paragraph about your favourite animal. Underline all of the nouns in the paragraph with yellow. Circle any plural nouns.

Name ______________________________

# Sports

**plural nouns**

A noun can be singular (one person, place, thing or idea) or plural (more than one). Usually, a noun becomes plural by adding an s to the end.

**Make the nouns plural.**

| | | | |
|---|---|---|---|
| skate | ______________ | club | ______________ |
| base | ______________ | racket | ______________ |
| hurdle | ______________ | guard | ______________ |
| helmet | ______________ | uniform | ______________ |

**Use the plural nouns to finish the sentences.**

Jackie and Manish need their ______________ to play tennis.

Javed needs shin ______________ to play football.

Bobby got new hockey ______________ for his birthday.

The team's softball ______________ are blue.

The cricket players' ______________ protected their heads.

Asen ran the ______________ after she hit a home run.

Omar wants his own set of golf ______________ .

Bijoy jumped over the ______________ during track practice.

## Review Work

Underline the other nouns in the sentences with yellow.

## Draft Book

Write a paragraph about your favourite sport. Underline all of the nouns in the paragraph with yellow.

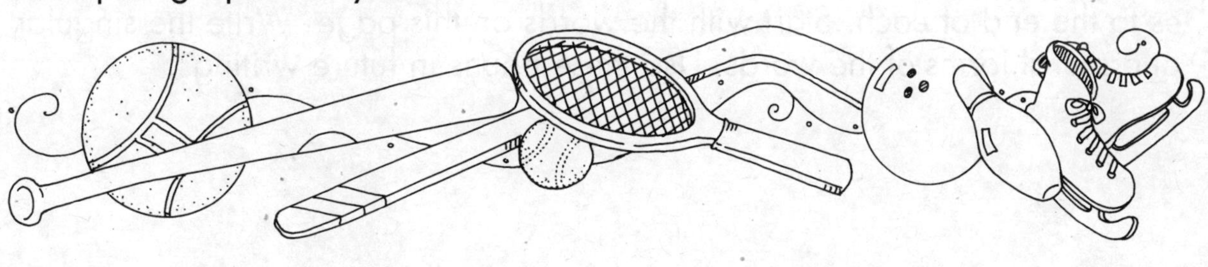

Name ________________________________

# Creatures

**plural nouns**

A noun can be singular (one person, place, thing or idea) or plural (more than one). Sometimes, a noun becomes plural by adding *es* to the end.

**example:** crutch → crut**ches** **example:** class → cla**sses**
**example:** dish → di**shes** **example:** box → bo**xes**

**Make the nouns plural.**

| | | | |
|---|---|---|---|
| lunch | ____________ | dash | ____________ |
| pouch | ____________ | crunch | ____________ |
| dress | ____________ | brush | ____________ |
| finch | ____________ | tax | ____________ |
| fox | ____________ | branch | ____________ |

**Use some of the plural nouns to finish the sentences.**

My dad packed ____________ for my brother and me.

There are three ____________ on the bathroom counter.

Kangaroos, opossums and koalas use their ____________ to carry their young.

The ____________ of the tree were filled with

____________ building nests.

## Review Work

Underline the other nouns in the sentences with yellow.

## Draft Book

Make a list of nouns that become plural by adding es to the end of each. Start with the words on this page. Write the singular and plural forms of the words. Use these nouns in future writings.

Name ______________________________

# Different Endings

**plural nouns**

A noun can be singular (one person, place, thing or idea) or plural (more than one). Usually, a noun becomes plural by adding an *s* to the end. A noun that ends with *ch*, *s*, *z*, *sh* or *x* becomes plural by adding *es* to the end. A noun that ends with *f* or *fe* becomes plural by changing the *f* or *fe* to *v* and adding *es* to the end.

**example:** calf → cal**ves** **example:** scarf → scar**ves**

**Make the nouns plural.**

| | | | |
|---|---|---|---|
| leaf | ______________ | coach | ______________ |
| half | ______________ | knife | ______________ |
| bench | ______________ | bunch | ______________ |
| glass | ______________ | lunch | ______________ |

**Write the other form of each noun.**

Red, yellow and orange ______________ (leaf) are falling from the trees.

Please put the ______________ (dish), ______________ (glass), ______________ (knife) and ______________ (fork) on the table.

For ______________ (lunches), Chitra had two ______________ (half) of a sandwich and a ______________ (bunches) of ______________ (grape).

**Review Work**
Draw a star above each singular noun in the sentences.

**Draft Book**
Two of the plural nouns were not used in the sentences.
Write a sentence with each word. Underline the nouns with yellow.

Name ______________________________

# Here Come the Ys

**plural nouns**

A noun can be singular (one person, place, thing or idea) or plural (more than one). There are two rules for making a noun that ends with *y* plural. For a noun that ends with a consonant + *y*, change the *y* to *i* and add *es* to the end. For a noun that ends with a vowel + *y*, add an *s* to the end.

**example:** lady → ladies **example:** toy → toys

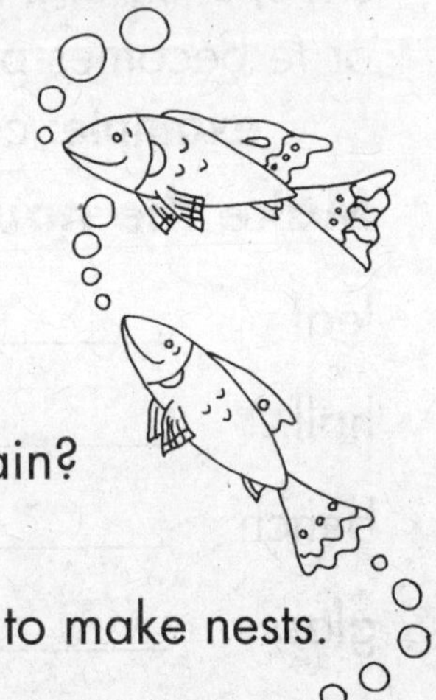

**Make the nouns plural.**

Tanya has seventeen ______________________ in her aquarium.
guppy

Did you forget your house ______________________ again?
key

Sometimes raccoons climb into ______________________ to make nests.
chimney

How many ______________________ do you have in your bank?
rupee

Wild ______________________ live in the woods by Jan's house.
turkey

Mridul loves to have ______________________ on his ice cream.
strawberry

Gopan has read many ______________________ about
story

______________________ living in the rain forests.
monkey

## Review Work

Underline the other nouns in the sentences with yellow. Draw a star above each singular noun.

## Draft Book

Make these nouns plural: baby, pony, boy and cherry. Use the plural nouns to write four sentences. Circle the plural nouns. Draw a star above each singular noun.

Name ______________________________

# Make Mine Plural

**plural nouns**

A noun can be singular (one person, place, thing or idea) or plural (more than one).

**Make the nouns plural.**

| | | | |
|---|---|---|---|
| mess | ________ | hobby | ________ |
| wish | ________ | thief | ________ |
| wife | ________ | donkey | ________ |
| peach | ________ | daisy | ________ |
| dog | ________ | mass | ________ |
| way | ________ | rash | ________ |
| berry | ________ | ray | ________ |
| life | ________ | baby | ________ |
| crash | ________ | sky | ________ |
| toy | ________ | watch | ________ |
| shelf | ________ | bay | ________ |
| class | ________ | candy | ________ |
| elf | ________ | day | ________ |

## Review Work

Write each singular noun from above that ends with *y* but does not have es when it becomes plural.

______________________________________________

______________________________________________

## Draft Book

Choose five pairs of nouns (a pair includes both singular and plural forms). Write a sentence with each noun.

Name ______________________________

# Tricky Nouns

## irregular plural nouns

A noun can be singular (one person, place, thing or idea) or plural (more than one). Some nouns become plural by changing the middles or the ends.

**example:** goose → geese  **example:** mouse → mice

Some nouns do not change when they become plural.

**examples:** cod, grouse, deer, fish, moose, series, sheep, swine

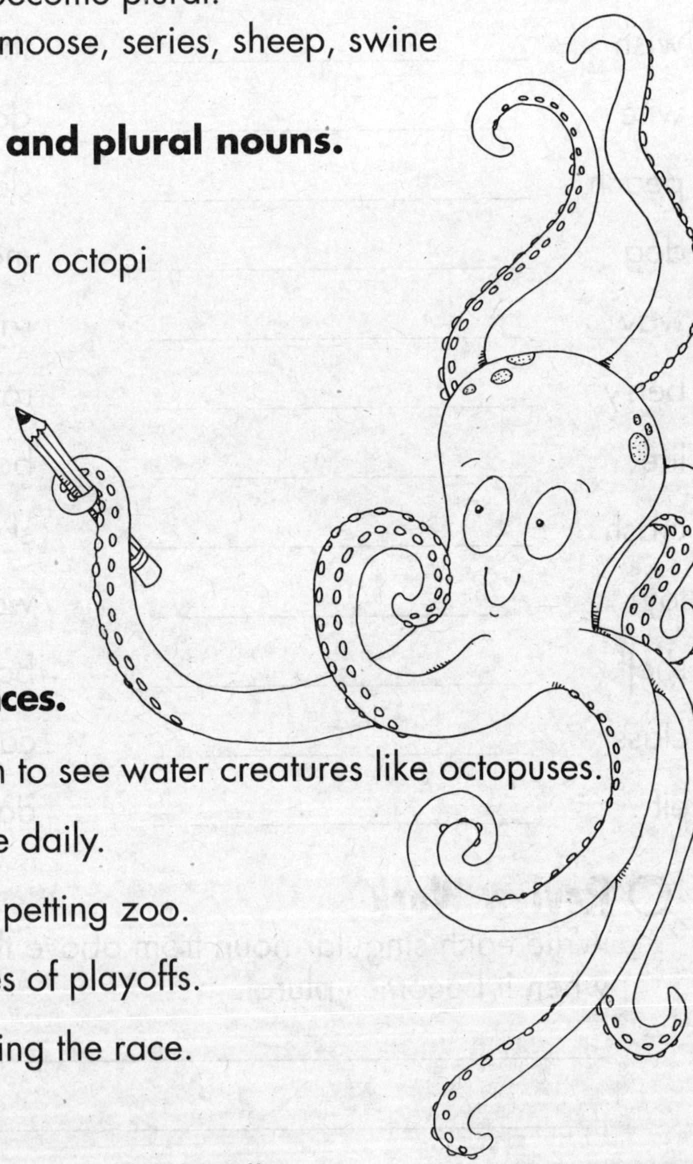

**Draw lines to match the singular and plural nouns.**

| | |
|---|---|
| ox | feet |
| tooth | octopuses or octopi |
| child | men |
| foot | buses |
| person | children |
| octopus | people |
| man | oxen |
| woman | women |
| bus | teeth |

**Circle the tricky nouns in the sentences.**

The children took buses to the aquarium to see water creatures like octopuses.

All people should brush their teeth twice daily.

Animals like deer and sheep are at the petting zoo.

Men lined up for tickets to the two series of playoffs.

The women rubbed their feet after running the race.

### Review Work

Underline the other nouns in the sentences with yellow.

### Draft Book

Write a story using some of the tricky nouns on this page. Underline the nouns with yellow. Circle the plural nouns. Draw a star above each singular noun.

Name ________________________________

# Mine, All Mine

**possessive nouns**

A possessive noun shows belonging. If a noun is singular or if it is plural but does not end with an *s*, add an apostrophe + *s* (*'s*) to the end to make it possessive.

**examples:** cat's food, boss's pen, men's shoes

If a noun is plural and already ends with an *s*, add an apostrophe to the end.

**examples:** cats' collars, players' helmets

**Finish each sentence with a possessive noun.**

The pond belongs to those frogs. It is the ____________________ pond.

The crayons belong Divya. They are ____________________ crayons.

The bats belong to those boys. They are the ____________________ bats.

The swing belongs to Manas. It is ____________________ swing.

The hill belongs to the ants. It is the ____________________ hill.

The hat belongs to Mohit. It is ____________________ hat.

Those marbles belong to Louis. They are ____________________ marbles.

**Make the nouns possessive.**

| | | | |
|---|---|---|---|
| girls | ____________________ | Kunal | ____________________ |
| frog | ____________________ | Yasar | ____________________ |
| dogs | ____________________ | classmates | ____________________ |
| women | ____________________ | Mr. Ram | ____________________ |
| Tara | ____________________ | birds | ____________________ |
| teachers | ____________________ | turtle | ____________________ |

## Review Work

Draw a star above each singular noun in the sentences. Circle the plural nouns.

## Draft Book

Write ten sentences with possessive nouns. Use both singular and plural nouns. Underline the nouns with yellow.

Name ______________________________

# Who Owns It? possessive nouns

A possessive noun shows belonging. If a noun is singular or if it is plural but does not end with an *s*, add an apostrophe + *s* ('*s*) to the end to make it possessive.

**examples:** cat's food, boss's pen, men's shoes

If a noun is plural and already ends with an *s*, add an apostrophe to the end.

**examples:** cats' collars, players' helmets

**Circle the possessive noun in each sentence. How many people or things possess something? Circle 1 if one person or thing possesses something. Circle 2+ if more than one person or thing possesses something.**

1 2+ The audience laughed at the comedian's performance.

1 2+ The turtles' pond needs a log in it.

1 2+ The dancer's shoes had holes in them.

1 2+ A book's pages must be treated gently.

1 2+ The chipmunks' home is stuffed with bird seed.

1 2+ Can you sharpen the students' pencils?

1 2+ The museum's admission price is Rs. 3.00.

1 2+ Lisa let Chirag's five birds out of their cages.

1 2+ The bluebird's nest has three eggs.

1 2+ Hakim borrowed the team's score book.

1 2+ Sandra washed her parents' cars.

1 2+ Omar's cat scratched me.

## Review Work

Underline the other nouns in the sentences with yellow.

## Draft Book

Choose four friends. Use possessive nouns to write sentences about things that belong to them. Write two sentences about each friend.

Name ___________________________

# Hide-and-Seek

**action verbs**

An action verb tells what someone or something is doing.

**example:** The boy **swings** the golf club.

**example:** The mouse **scampers** across the floor.

**Circle each action verb.**

Varun hides from his friend.

Manisha searches for the others.

Jaya crouches behind the slide.

Ram crawls along the fence.

Salma jumps over the log.

Insects scatter out of the way.

Maria giggles behind the oak tree.

Joy climbs up the old maple.

The leaves on the old maple sway in the breeze.

Manisha finds Karan.

Karan races to the free spot.

Manisha tags Karan.

Karan yells for everyone to come out.

## Review Work

Underline the nouns in the sentences with yellow.

## Draft Book

Find a page in your Draft Book with the nouns underlined with yellow. Underline the verbs with blue.

Name ____________________________________

# Thunderstorm

**action verbs**

An action verb tells what someone or something is doing.

**Use the verbs to finish the sentences. Use each verb only once.**

| whips | flashes | observes | pound |
|---|---|---|---|
| scurries | booms | crash | shine |
| slap | race | reports | hide |

Jason ____________________________ the storm from his bedroom window.

The meteorologist ____________________________ the arrival of the storm.

Storm clouds ____________________________ across the sky.

Lightning ____________________________ in the distance.

Thunder ____________________________ loudly.

Raindrops ____________________________ the rooftops.

Jyotsna ____________________________ to find candles.

Wet branches ____________________________ the windowpanes.

Stars ____________________________ unseen behind the clouds.

The waves ____________________________ against the shore.

The puppies ____________________________ under the couch.

The wind ____________________________ the waves into whitecaps.

## Review Work

Draw a star above each singular noun in the sentences.
Circle the plural nouns.

## Draft Book

Find a page in your Draft Book with the nouns underlined with yellow. Underline the verbs with blue.

Name ______________________________

# Entomologist

**linking verbs**

Linking verbs are verbs that do not show action. They express a state of being (to be). A linking verb connects, or links, two parts of a sentence.

Most linking verbs are forms of *to be*. There are eight forms of the verb *to be*: *am, are, is, was, were, (will) be, (am, are, was, were) being, (have, has, had) been*.

**example:** I **am** left-handed. **example:** He **is** an artist.
**example:** You **are** a gymnast. **example:** We **are** best friends.

**Circle the linking verbs in the sentences.**

I am an entomologist. An entomologist studies insects.

Insects are the most plentiful creatures on Earth.

A camera with a macro lens is an entomologist's tool.

A honeycomb cell is a home for one honeybee egg.

Larvae are baby insects that have hatched from eggs.

Monarchs are migrating butterflies.

A bee is a flying insect that can sting you.

A moth is different from a butterfly.

All ladybugs are not female.

Spiders are not insects. They are arachnids.

A pupa is the stage between larva and adult.

Who knew there was so much to learn about insects?

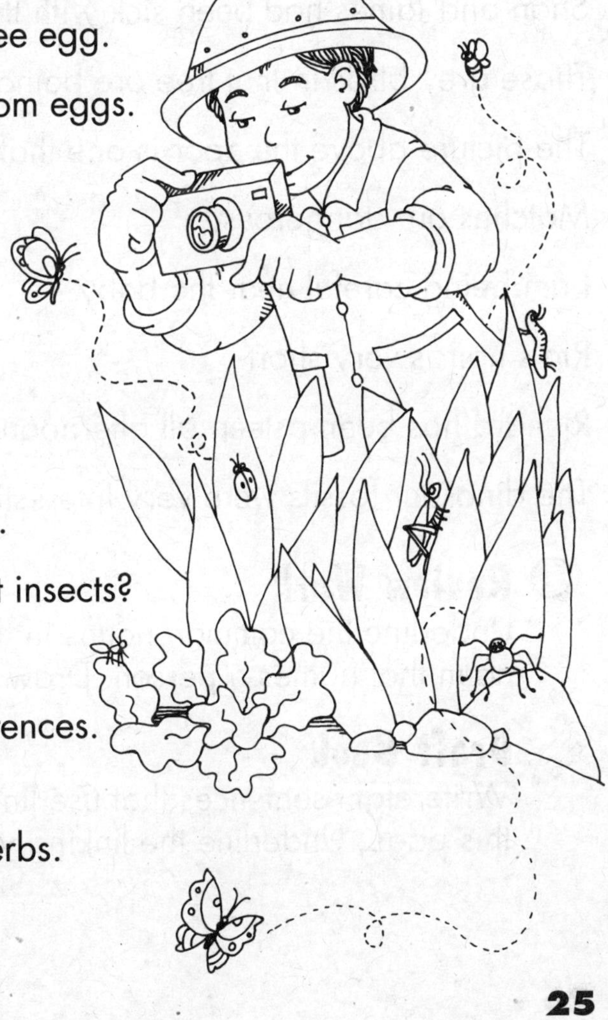

## Review Work

Underline the common nouns in the sentences.

## Draft Book

Write eight sentences that use linking verbs.
Underline the linking verbs with blue.

Name ________________________________

# Link Them Together linking verbs

Linking verbs are verbs that do not show action. They express a state of being. A linking verb connects, or links, two parts of a sentence. In a sentence, a linking verb comes before a noun or adjective—not an action verb.

Most linking verbs are forms of *to be*. There are eight forms of the verb *to be*: *am*, *are*, *is*, *was*, *were*, (*will*) *be*, (*am*, *are*, *was*, *were*) *being*, (*have*, *has*, *had*) *been*.

**Circle the linking verbs in the sentences.**

Rena was in the gym.

The garbage cans were full.

Hannah will be in second grade next year.

We have been patient.

Shan and James had been sick with the flu.

Those grey birds in that tree are being very noisy.

The picture above the door is one that I painted.

Matches are dangerous.

I am being careful near the baby.

Ria's hair is very short.

Richard has been asleep all afternoon.

The dinosaur fossils were very interesting.

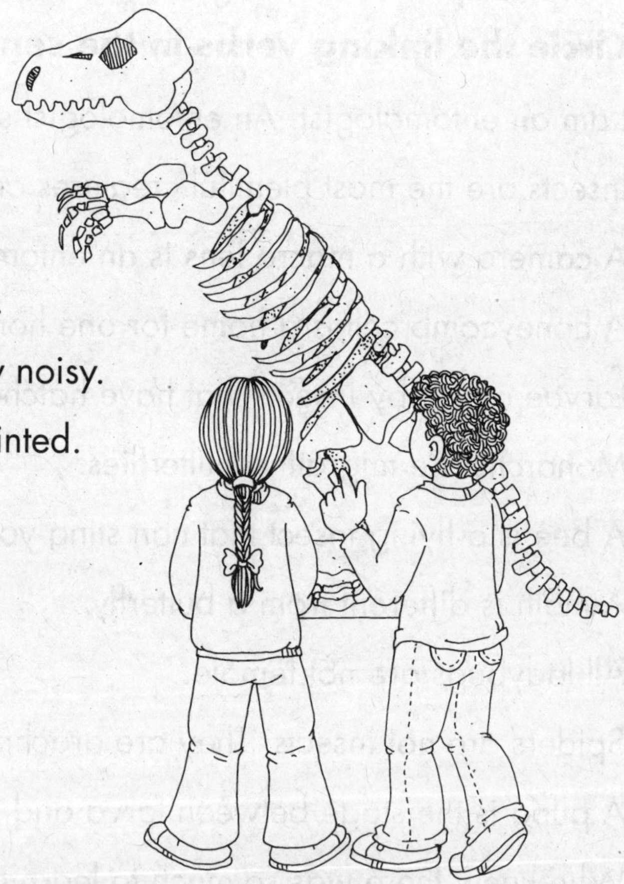

## Review Work

Underline the common nouns in the sentences. Draw an X next to each proper noun that names a person. Draw a tick next to the possessive noun.

## Draft Book

Write eight sentences that use linking verbs. Use a variety of the verbs from this page. Underline the linking verbs with blue.

Name ______________________________

# Artwork

**linking verbs**

Linking verbs are verbs that do not show action. They express a state of being. A linking verb connects, or links, two parts of a sentence. In a sentence, a linking verb comes before a noun or adjective—not an action verb.

Most linking verbs are forms of *to be*. There are eight forms of the verb *to be*: *am, are, is, was, were,* (*will*) *be,* (*am, are, was, were*) *being,* (*have, has, had*) *been*. Other linking verbs include forms of these verbs: *to appear, to become, to feel, to grow, to look, to remain, to seem, to smell, to sound, to taste*.

**Circle the linking verbs in the sentences.**

The art projects will remain in the classroom.

The pots in the kiln became too hot to touch.

The clay appeared hard, but it was really soft.

The moulded bird with two heads looks unusual.

Nandu sanded the wood table until it felt smooth.

Those ceramic wind chimes sound beautiful.

This glaze seems dry.

Many students become fans of art.

Those markers smell awful.

All of this artwork looks great!

Jay looks happy when he's painting.

## Review Work

Underline the nouns with yellow.

## Draft Book

Write 10 sentences that use linking verbs. Use a variety of the verbs from this page. Underline the linking verbs with blue.

Name ________________________________

# Lend a Hand

**helping verbs**

Helping verbs are verbs that help main verbs express tenses. There are 23 helping verbs. *Would*, *should*, *shall* and *will* are helping verbs. Forms of the following verbs are also helping verbs:

| | |
|---|---|
| be: | am, are, is, was, were, be, being, been |
| do: | do, does, did |
| have: | have, has, had |
| may: | may, must, might |
| can: | can, could |

**Circle the helping verb in each sentence. Draw an arrow to the verb it is helping.**

That area under the trees would make a good picnic spot.

Those crickets are making a lot of noise.

Amina has eaten her sandwich already.

Kiran might buy a new bike.

Sheila is sneezing.

Charu can chop nuts for the banana bread.

Matthew could answer that question for you.

Hanif's kitten had shredded the magazine.

Renu should rake the leaves this weekend.

Ajay was coughing all night.

## Review Work

Underline the nouns in the sentences with yellow.

## Draft Book

Write five sentences with helping verbs. In each sentence, underline the helping verb and the verb being helped with blue.

Name ____________________

# Lots of Help

**helping verbs**

Helping verbs are verbs that help main verbs express tenses. There are 23 helping verbs. *Would*, *should*, *shall* and *will* are helping verbs. Forms of the following verbs are also helping verbs:

be: am, are, is, was, were, be, being, been
do: do, does, did
have: have, has, had
may: may, must, might
can: can, could

Up to three helping verbs can be used at one time.

**example:** Anne **was** crying.
**example:** Preet **should have** cut the grass.
**example:** Dolly **will have been** sleeping for an hour when you finish.

**Circle the helping verb(s) in each sentence. Draw an arrow to the verb being helped.**

The cactus wrens in that old saguaro cactus are protected from predators.

The clay tiles are being mounted behind the sink in the kitchen.

Those fern fossils may have been found in sedimentary rocks.

Toothbrushes should be changed every two to three months.

Rekha and Naureen will be sleeping in that tent.

The red squirrel could have been hit by that car.

Nikhil and Alok were picking strawberries.

We may be going to the beach.

That huge oak tree must have fallen during the storm.

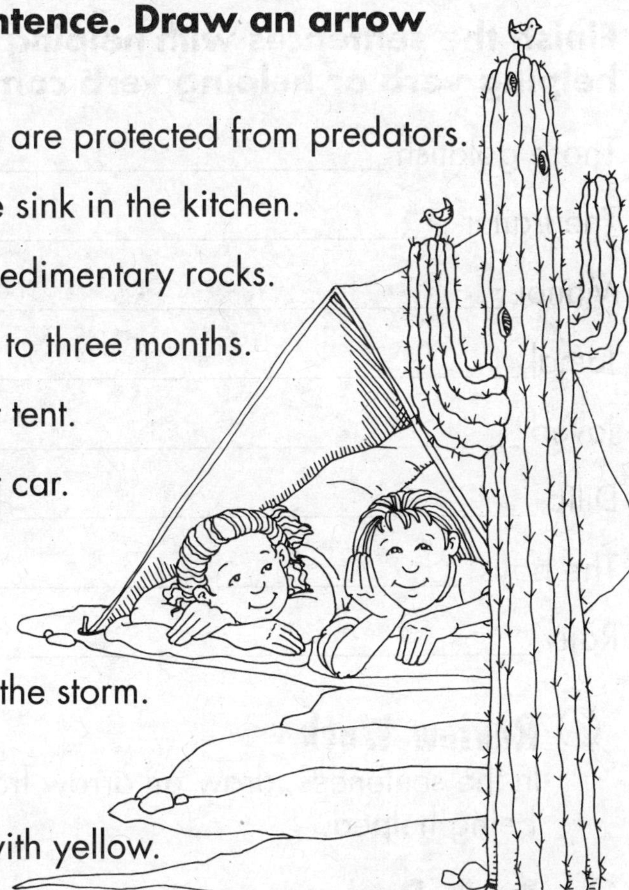

## Review Work

Underline the nouns in the sentences with yellow.

## Draft Book

Write eight sentences with helping verbs. In each sentence, underline the helping verb(s) and the verb being helped with blue.

Name ____________________

# You're Helping

**helping verbs**

Helping verbs are verbs that help main verbs express tenses. There are 23 helping verbs. *Would*, *should*, *shall* and *will* are helping verbs. Forms of the following verbs are also helping verbs:

be: am, are, is, was, were, be, being, been
do: do, does, did
have: have, has, had
may: may, must, might
can: can, could

Up to three helping verbs can be used at one time.

**example:** Tina **is** practising her dance routine.
**example:** Amar **could be** hiding behind the gazebo.
**example:** Tarun **would have been** hiking if he hadn't got sick.

**Finish the sentences with helping verbs. Use a different helping verb or helping verb combination in each sentence.**

Those goldfish ____________________ swimming through the water.

The trailer ____________________ attached to the trailer hitch.

Manoj ____________________ go to the movie.

Jamal ____________________ ride his scooter.

Javed ____________________ clear the table.

Dilip ____________________ baking cookies.

The boys ____________________ racing their toy cars.

Rajiv ____________________ turned on the light.

## Review Work

In the sentences, draw an arrow from the helping verb(s) to the verb being helped.

## Draft Book

Write 10 sentences with helping verbs. In each sentence, underline the helping verb(s) and the verb being helped with blue.

Name ____________________________________

# Now and Then

**past and present tense**

Verbs use tenses to tell when something is happening. When the action happens now, it is present tense. When the action happened in the past, it is past tense. One way to make a verb past tense is to add *ed* to the end.

**example:** Suman **studies** for the test. (present tense)
**example:** Suman **studied** for the test. (past tense)

**Circle the verb in each sentence. Write whether the verb is past tense or present tense.**

The sea horse floats by the starfish. ____________________

The paper's colour faded in the sunlight. ____________________

The string tangled into a huge knot. ____________________

Nilesh disturbed the sleeping puppy. ____________________

The kites dance in the breeze. ____________________

Sohan sharpens his pencil. ____________________

Asha bandaged her finger. ____________________

Children tumble down the sand dune. ____________________

Vishal flicked the paper football. ____________________

Gautam defends his snow fort. ____________________

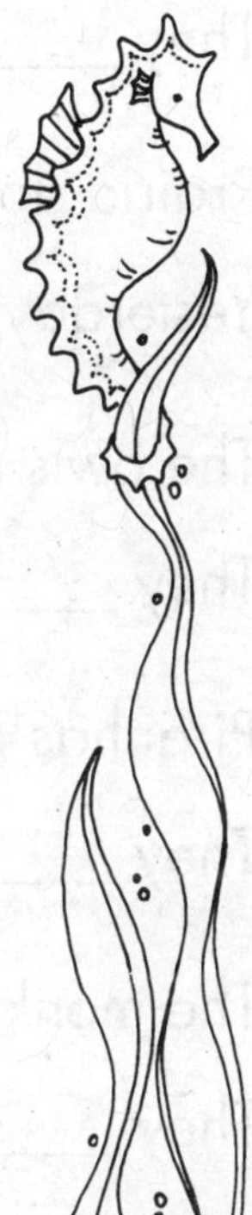

## Review Work

Underline the nouns in the sentences with yellow.

## Draft Book

Choose five of the sentences. If the verb is present tense, rewrite it in the past tense. If the verb is past tense, rewrite it in the present tense.

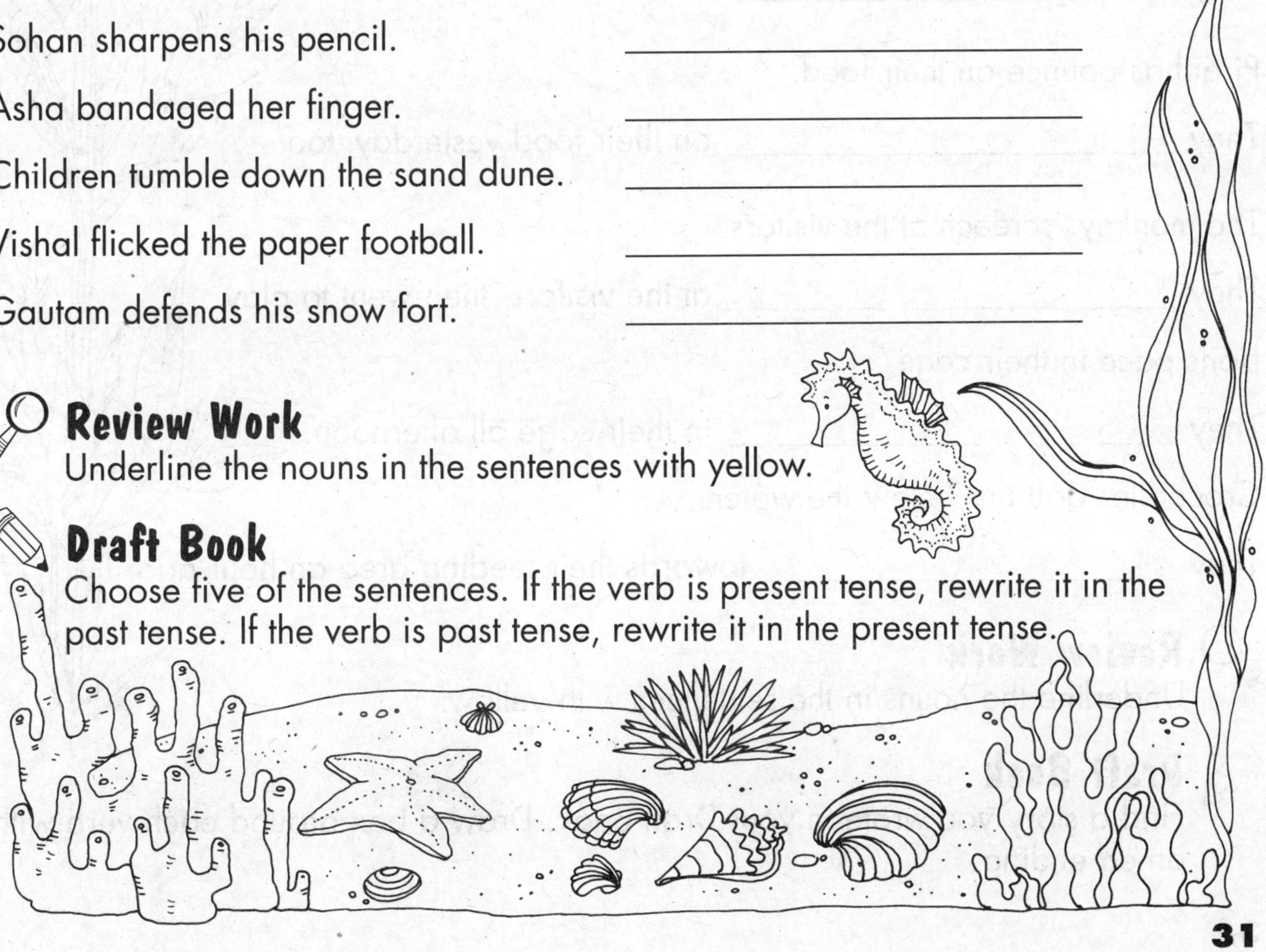

Name ______________________________

# At the Zoo

**past and present tense**

Verbs use tenses to tell when something is happening. When the action happens now, it is present tense. When the action happened in the past, it is past tense. One way to make a verb past tense is to add *ed* to the end.

**Underline the present tense verb in the first sentence. Add *ed* to make the verb past tense in the second sentence.**

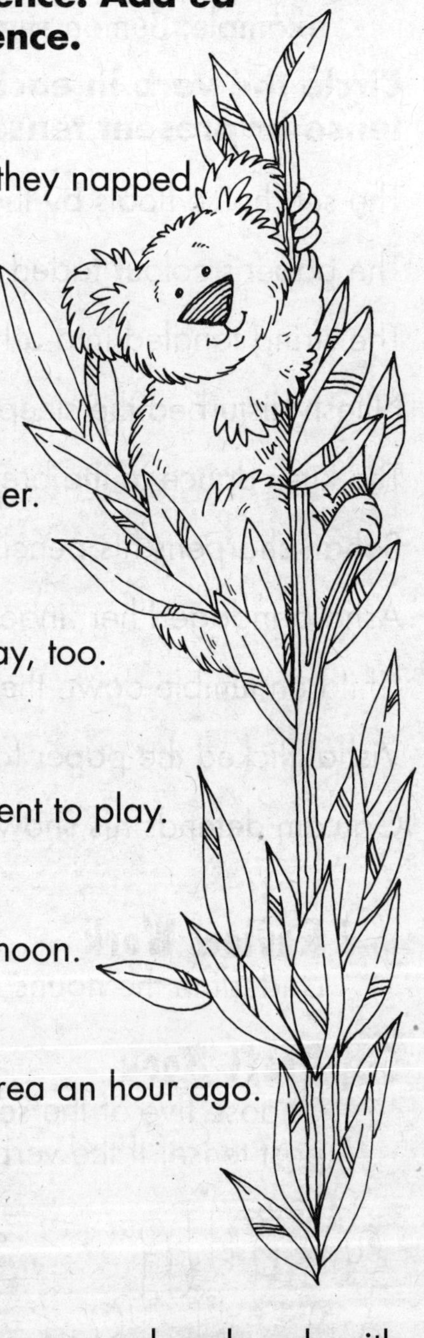

The koalas munch on eucalyptus leaves.

They ________________________ on the leaves before they napped.

Prairie dogs burrow in the dirt.

Yesterday, they ________________________ for hours.

The owls rest in the shade.

They ________________________ in the shade last summer.

Piranhas pounce on their food.

They ________________________ on their food yesterday, too.

The monkeys screech at the visitors.

They ________________________ at the visitors, then went to play.

Lions pace in their cage.

They ________________________ in their cage all afternoon.

Crocodiles drift just below the water.

They ________________________ towards their feeding area an hour ago.

### Review Work

Underline the nouns in the sentences with yellow.

### Draft Book

Find a story you wrote in your Draft Book. Draw a box around each verb with an *ed* ending.

Name ________________________________

# Pick the Right Verb

**past and present tense**

Verbs use tenses to tell when something is happening. When the action happens now, it is present tense. When the action happened in the past, it is past tense. One way to make a verb past tense is to add *ed* to the end.

**example:** Amy **hugs** her baby sister. (present tense)
**example:** Amy **hugged** her baby sister. (past tense)

**Circle the correct verb in each sentence.**

Don't (play, played) with your pencil.

The boxers (punch, punched) the punching bags before they stepped in the ring.

Sweta (slumps, slumped) in her chair when she heard about the quiz.

Jaya washes the windows, and Sreenu (mops, mopped) the floor.

Mohan (hunts, hunted) for his homework when the teacher asked for it.

I like to watch boats (cruise, cruised) through that channel.

Last week, Hema and Anand (hike, hiked) in Pratt Park.

Prakash was grounded because he (teases, teased) his sister.

Naresh and Lavanya (soak, soaked) in the hot tub last night.

Jamal watches the movie, but Ratish (snoozes, snoozed) through it.

## Review Work

Underline the word or words that helped you decide whether each sentence needed a present or past tense verb.

## Draft Book

Write a story using verbs with *ed* endings. Draw a box around each past tense verb.

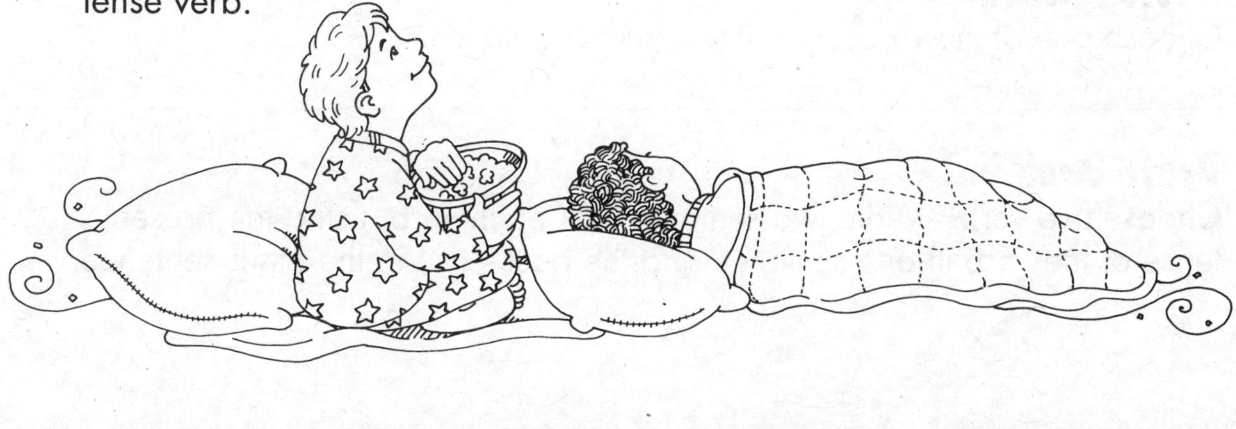

Name ______________________________

# Telling Time

**past tense**

Verb tenses tell when something is happening. When the action happens now, it is present tense. When the action happened in the past, it is past tense. There are several ways to add *ed* to a verb to make it past tense.

Most verbs add *ed* or *d* to the ends of the base words.

**example:** box + ed = boxed **example:** wave + d = waved

If a verb ends with a consonant + *y*, change *y* to *i* and add *ed* to the end.

**example:** carry + ed = carried **example:** bury + ed = buried

If a verb ends with a short vowel + one consonant, double the consonant and add *ed* to the end.

**example:** tip + ed = tipped **example:** stop + ed = stopped

**Change these verbs to the past tense.**

| breathe | chip | hurry |
|---|---|---|
| ______ | ______ | ______ |
| cruise | tap | dry |
| ______ | ______ | ______ |
| parachute | toast | play |
| ______ | ______ | ______ |
| trip | comb | copy |
| ______ | ______ | ______ |
| shop | try | pounce |
| ______ | ______ | ______ |

## Review Work

Choose one of the verbs. Use it to write a sentence.

______________________________

## Draft Book

Choose five verbs. Write two sentences for each verb, using the present tense of the verb in one sentence and the past tense in the other sentence.

Name ______________________________

# Busy, Busy

**past tense**

Verb tenses tell when something is happening. When the action happens now, it is present tense. When the action happened in the past, it is past tense. There are several ways to add *ed* to a verb to make it past tense.

Most verbs add *ed* or *d* to the ends of the base words.

**example:** box + ed = boxed **example:** wave + d = waved

If a verb ends with a consonant + *y*, change *y* to *i* and add *ed* to the end.

**example:** carry + ed = carried **example:** bury + ed = buried

If a verb ends with a short vowel + one consonant, double the consonant and add *ed* to the end.

**example:** tip + ed = tipped **example:** stop + ed = stopped

**Make the verbs past tense to finish the sentences.**

study Nadiya ______________________ the bud with a magnifying glass.

copy George ______________________ his partner's actions.

trim Nigel ______________________ the cat's claws.

rake Surya ______________________ the leaves.

skip Malar ______________________ down the hall.

chop Vinod ______________________ onions and peppers for pizza.

frame Binoy______________________ the class photo.

grab Jessie______________________ the dog's leash.

empty Isha ______________________ the aquarium.

whine Poppy ______________________ for her bone.

### Review Work

Underline the nouns in the sentences with yellow.

### Draft Book

Write six sentences using verbs in the past tense.

Name ________________________________

# Tricky Verbs

**past tense**

Verb tenses tell when something is happening. When the action happens now, it is present tense. When the action happened in the past, it is past tense. One way to make a verb past tense is to add *ed* to the end. An irregular verb becomes past tense by changing its spelling.

**example:** Brinda **rings** the bell. (present tense)
**example:** Brinda **rang** the bell. (past tense)

**example:** Roshan **swims** across the pool. (present tense)
**example:** Roshan **swam** across the pool. (past tense)

**Write the past tense of the irregular verbs to finish the sentences.**

Geeta ________________________ (tell) us about the book she read.

Anand ________________________ (take) the last cookie.

Tara ________________________ (run) around the bases.

Gopi ________________________ (give) me his spot in line.

Lasar ________________________ (come) to school late.

Aman ________________________ (sing) in the choir.

Tony ________________________ (meet) the new principal.

Soni ________________________ (begin) to work hard.

Tarun ________________________ (know) how to fix the sharpener.

Probal ________________________ (leave) his soccer cleats at home.

Arvind ________________________ (write) a great poem.

Sameera ________________________ (sit) on the new couch.

## Review Work

Underline the nouns in the sentences with yellow.

## Draft Book

Choose five irregular verbs from this page. Write one sentence using the present tense and one sentence using the past tense of each verb.

Name ____________________

# More Tricky Verbs

**past tense**

Verb tenses tell when something is happening. When the action happens now, it is present tense. When the action happened in the past, it is past tense. One way to make a verb past tense is to add *ed* to the end. An irregular verb becomes past tense by changing its spelling.

**examples:** bite / bit     bring / brought     drink / drank

**Write the past tense of the irregular verbs to finish the sentences.**

Mrs. Wahid ____________________ me to understand fractions.
teaches

Grandpa ____________________ a bunch of fish.
catches

The elephant ____________________ the chain.
breaks

Many monkeys ____________________ through the trees.
swing

The kickball players ____________________ teams during recess.
choose

The children ____________________ down the hill on a sled.
slide

Krishna ____________________ the ball to Hajira.
throws

The allergy shot ____________________ for just a minute.
stings

Bipin ____________________ up when his alarm clock rang.
wakes

## Review Work

Underline the nouns with yellow.

## Draft Book

Write your own past tense sentence with each irregular verb from this page. Underline the verbs with blue.

Name ______________________________

# Under the Sea

**future tense**

Verb tenses tell when something is happening. When the action is going to happen in the future, it is future tense. The helping verb *will* is added before the main verb to make the future tense. If the noun is singular, the s is dropped before adding *will*.

**example:** Dad **mows** the lawn. (present)
**example:** Dad **will mow** the lawn. (future)

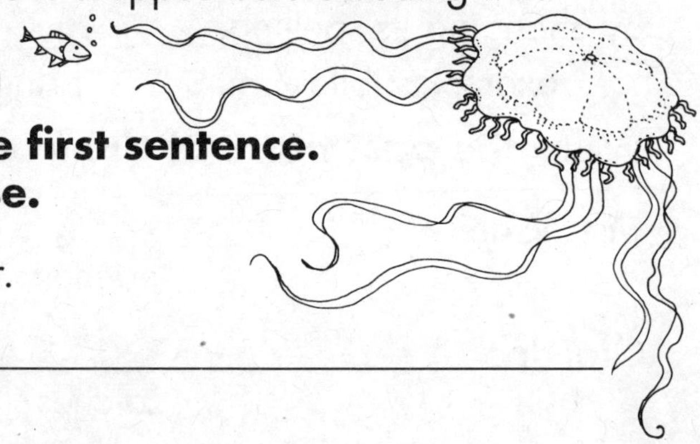

**Underline the present tense verb in the first sentence. Rewrite the sentence in the future tense.**

present tense: Sharks swim through the water.

future tense: ______________________________

present tense: Jellyfish float on the currents.

future tense: ______________________________

present tense: Manta rays sail through the water.

future tense: ______________________________

present tense: Sea slugs meander along the bottom.

future tense: ______________________________

present tense: Anemones prey on unwary fish.

future tense: ______________________________

present tense: Octopuses squirt ink.

future tense: ______________________________

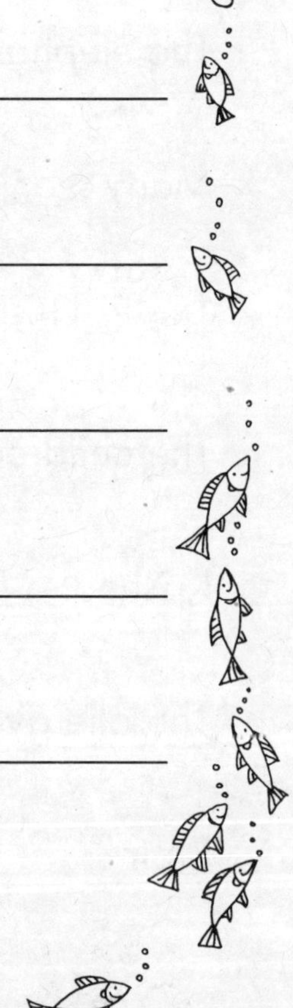

## Review Work

Write the past tense of each verb from the sentences.

## Draft Book

Write five sentences using verbs in the future tense. Put the helping word *will* in front of each verb. Underline the verbs with blue, including the word *will*.

Name ______________________________

# Which Is Correct?

**past and future tense**

Verb tenses tell when something is happening. When the action is going to happen in the future, it is future tense. The helping verb *will* is added before the main verb to make the future tense. If the noun is singular, the *s* is dropped before adding *will*.

**example:** Charulata **eats** the cake. (present)
**example:** Charulata **will eat** the cake. (future)

**Circle the correct verb in each sentence.**

I (complete, will complete) my homework tonight.

Hari already (filled, will fill) the pails with sand to make a castle.

Kiran's parents (tried, will try) to contact her coach tomorrow.

Julie (ate, will eat) pizza for lunch yesterday.

Mr. Zeer (draw, will draw) plans for a new house this summer.

Sajida (began, will begin) work on her project last Thursday.

Next week, Swaroop and John (hiked, will hike) on the trail.

Madhu (watches, will watch) the movie next Friday.

Last year, it (rained, will rain) during our family vacation.

Mita (open, will open) presents on her birthday.

## Review Work

Underline the word or words that helped you decide whether each sentence needed a past or future tense verb.

## Draft Book

Write your own sentence with each future tense verb from this page.

Name ____________________

# Space Trip

**future tense**

Verb tenses tell when something is happening. When the action is going to happen in the future, it is future tense. The helping verb *will* is added before the main verb to make the future tense. If the noun is singular, the *s* is dropped before adding *will*.

**example:** Sabu **raked** the lawn. (past)
**example:** Sabu **will rake** the lawn. (future)

**Write the correct future tense verb on the line.**

Irfan has plans to go into space.

A group (built) ____________________ a huge rocket.

Technicians (checked) ____________________ safety issues.

Irfan and his dad (mapped) ____________________ the journey ahead of time.

Irfan and his friends (boarded) ____________________ the rocket.

The announcer (counted) ____________________ down to zero.

The rocket (exploded) ____________________ into orbit.

The crew (viewed) ____________________ Earth from space.

They (observed) ____________________ comets and asteroids.

Irfan (kept) ____________________ a day-to-day journal.

Mahesh (recorded) ____________________ space sounds.

Romila (photographed) ____________________ interesting things.

Jyotsna (collected) ____________________ space dust.

They (returned) ____________________ to Earth with many photos, recordings, items and stories.

## Review Work

Underline the nouns with yellow.

## Draft Book

Write about your own imaginary trip using future tense.

Name ______________________________

# Past, Present or Future verb tenses

Verb tenses tell when something is happening.

**Underline the verbs in the sentences. If the verb is future tense, underline both the main verb and the helping verb *will*. Circle past, present or future.**

| | | | |
|---|---|---|---|
| Vinita signed her name on the card. | **past** | **present** | **future** |
| Garg will golf in the tournament. | **past** | **present** | **future** |
| Magan snaps the links together. | **past** | **present** | **future** |
| Suhan climbs into his bunk bed. | **past** | **present** | **future** |
| Leena will set her alarm clock. | **past** | **present** | **future** |
| Kavita rocked her puppy to sleep. | **past** | **present** | **future** |
| Jaya will dip the strawberries in chocolate. | **past** | **present** | **future** |
| Raman catches a squirrel. | **past** | **present** | **future** |
| Sita calculated the answer. | **past** | **present** | **future** |
| Farhan will input the test. | **past** | **present** | **future** |
| Lisa will prepare lunch. | **past** | **present** | **future** |
| Roshan pestered his mother. | **past** | **present** | **future** |
| Smita sealed the envelope. | **past** | **present** | **future** |
| Sarita will polish her fingernails. | **past** | **present** | **future** |
| Mohit will spend the night at a friend's house. | **past** | **present** | **future** |

## Review Work

Underline the nouns with yellow.

## Draft Book

Write two sentences for each verb tense. Underline the verbs with blue. Label the sentences past tense, present tense or future tense.

Name ______________________________

# Not, Not, Not!

**contractions**

A contraction is two words that are put together to form one word. Some of the letters drop out of the second word when the words are joined. An apostrophe replaces those letters.

The word *not* forms a contraction with many helping or linking verbs.

**example:** did + not = didn't

The contraction for *will not* is an exception: will + not = won't.

**Add *n't* to the helping or linking verbs to make contractions.**

are ______________________ is ______________________

was ______________________ were ______________________

do ______________________ does ______________________

can ______________________ had ______________________

has ______________________ should ______________________

**Write a contraction for each sentence. Try to use each contraction only once.**

Sarat and Jamila ______________________ follow the directions.

Nirad ______________________ canoe without a life jacket.

Anant ______________________ know how to cook.

Malini ______________________ very hungry.

Nur ______________________ phoned me yet.

Merin ______________________ tired.

Mia ______________________ cleaned the horse stall when I left.

## Review Work

Find the other verbs in the sentences. Underline them with blue.

## Draft Book

Choose six contractions. Write a sentence with each one.

Name ______________________________

# Throw Some Out

**contractions**

A contraction is two words that are put together to form one word. Some of the letters drop out of the second word when the words are joined. An apostrophe replaces those letters. The following letters are left with the apostrophe when a contraction is made:

**n't** when you add *not* (is**n't**)
**'d** when you add *would* or *had* (we**'d**)
**'re** when you add *are* (we**'re**)
**'ll** when you add *will* (she**'ll**)
**'s** when you add *is* or *has* (it**'s**)
**'ve** when you add *have* (I**'ve**)

**Combine the words to make contractions.**

I + will = ________________
they + are = ________________
he + will = ________________
I + had = ________________
what + is = ________________
could + not = ________________
he + is = ________________
they + have = ________________
she + has = ________________
they + would = ________________
here + is = ________________
they + will = ________________

**Write the correct contraction on the line in each sentence.**

Chetan **should not** ________________ ride his skateboard without a helmet.

Arun **did not** ________________ remember to do her homework.

That is the strangest thing **I have** ________________ ever seen!

Do you think **they are** ________________ coming to the game?

I think **I will** ________________ buy a new backpack.

**Who is** ________________ on the telephone?

**Review Work**

Underline the action verbs in the sentences with blue.

**Draft Book**

Choose eight contractions. Write a sentence with each one.

Name ________________________________

# What We're Doing

**verb endings**

A verb follows the same rules as a noun when adding *s* or *es* to the end.

Add *s* to the ends of most verbs. **example:** run + s = runs

Add *es* to the end if the verb ends with *sh*, *s*, *z*, *ch* or *x*. **example:** pitch + es = pitches

Change *y* to *i* and add *es* to the end if the verb ends with a consonant + *y*. **example:** try + es = tries

Add *s* to the end if the verb ends with a vowel + *y*. **example:** enjoy + s = enjoys

**Finish each sentence with the verb and its correct ending.**

| | |
|---|---|
| **crunch** | Anna ____________________ on a carrot. |
| **fly** | Amina ____________________ her kite. |
| **toy** | Soni ____________________ with his food. |
| **fix** | Nilima ____________________ her bicycle. |
| **dish** | Vinod ____________________ out the spaghetti. |
| **play** | Vineeta ____________________ the piano. |
| **buzz** | Paul ____________________ like a bee. |
| **teach** | Sneha ____________________ her brother to tie his shoes. |
| **finish** | Rahman ____________________ his ice cream. |
| **pass** | Wahida ____________________ the football. |
| **spy** | Anita ____________________ on her friends. |

## Review Work

What kind of verb is used in each sentence?
Circle the correct answer.

action linking helping

## Draft Book

Write five sentences. Use singular nouns and verbs with the correct endings. Use the rules on this page.

Name ______________________________

# Twilight

**noun and verb agreement**

A singular noun uses a verb that has an *s* at the end.

**example:** The boy **climbs** the tree.

A plural noun uses a verb that does not have an *s* at the end.

**example:** The boys **climb** the tree.

**Circle the correct verb(s) in each sentence.**

Fluffy white clouds (drift, drifts) along.

The sun (fade, fades) behind the horizon.

A dog (bound, bounds) into the yard.

The door (open, opens).

The boy (hear, hears) many sounds.

Buddy (run, runs) into the woods and Kamal (follow, follows).

Kamal (walk, walks) out after his dog, Buddy.

Owls (call, calls) to one another.

Insects (buzz, buzzes) and (hum, hums).

Bullfrogs (croak, croaks).

The two friends (return, returns) home in soft darkness.

Stars (twinkle, twinkles) in the sky.

Kamal (call, calls) quietly to Buddy.

Buddy (reenter, reenters) the house with Kamal.

## Review Work

Underline the nouns in the sentences with yellow.

## Draft Book

Choose five of the sentences. Rewrite each one so that the first noun becomes the opposite (singular or plural) of what it is now. Make sure the verb has the correct ending to agree with the new noun.

Name ______________________________

# How You Exercise

**noun and verb agreement**

A singular noun uses a verb that has an *s* at the end.

**example:** The girl **runs** in the race.

A plural noun uses a verb that does not have an *s* at the end.

**example:** The girls **run** in the race.

**Use some of the verbs to finish the sentences. Add an *s* to the end of each verb if it is needed. Use each verb only once.**

| balance | bounce | climb | flip | sit | race | jump |
|---|---|---|---|---|---|---|
| hit | pitch | shoot | leap | roll | tie | lie |

The girls ______________________ their shoes for a walk.

Sana ______________________ the baseball to the batter.

Neha ______________________ the ball with the bat.

Kapil ______________________ the rope.

Ravi ______________________ the basketball.

The basketball players ______________________ baskets.

The runners ______________________ to the finish line.

Apu ______________________ over the hurdles.

Kamal ______________________ on the beam.

Mudit's classmates ______________________ on the mat for sit-ups.

Ayan ______________________ off the bars.

Vineet's friends ______________________ down the hill.

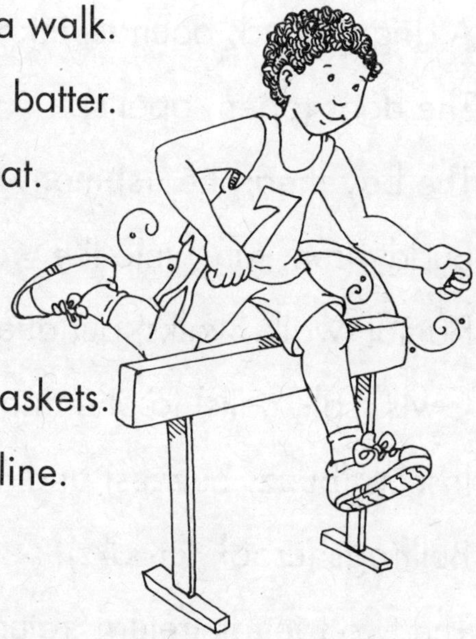

## Review Work

Underline the common nouns in the sentences. Draw an X next to each proper noun that names a person.

## Draft Book

Write eight sentences using both singular and plural nouns. Make sure the verbs have the correct endings to agree with the nouns.

Name ________________________________

# Five Senses

**noun and verb agreement**

A singular noun uses a verb that has an *s* at the end. A plural noun uses a verb that does not have an *s* at the end.

**Choose the correct noun and verb to finish each sentence. Write the words on the lines.**

The horse's ____________ ____________ the apple.
tooth / teeth chomps / chomp

Salman's right ____________ ____________ better than his left eye.
eye / eyes see / sees

Paul's left ____________ ____________ when he doesn't believe you.
eyebrow / eyebrows lift / lifts

A rabbit's two long ____________ can ____________ a fox coming.
ear / ears hear / hears

My ____________ ____________ something good.
nose / noses smells / smell

Our ____________ can ____________ freshly baked cookies.
mouth / mouths taste / tastes

All of our ____________ ____________ in the sand.
toe / toes wiggle / wiggles

The baby's five little ____________ ____________ her cheek.
finger / fingers touches / touch

## Review Work

Underline the singular nouns in the sentences with yellow.

## Draft Book

Write a story. Underline the nouns in the story with yellow. Underline the verbs with blue. Make sure your nouns and verbs agree.

Name ___________________________

# Describers

**adjectives**

Adjectives are words that describe nouns. Adjectives tell what kind, how many or which one. They can include number, colour, size, shape or other detail words.

**example:** The **dirty** puppy needs a bath.

**example:** The **public** library is closed today.

A sentence can have more than one adjective: **Four**, **grey** bugs are in the **small** garden.

**Circle the adjectives. Draw an arrow from the adjective to the noun it describes.**

An excited Devan opened the wrapped package.

Many tiny ants crawled across the jelly sandwich.

A bothersome mosquito buzzes near my ear.

The sweet, sticky cotton candy is gone.

Wahid has dirty socks and muddy shoes in that bag.

Four spotted dalmatians rode on the noisy, red fire engine.

Ram used the sharp scissors to cut the thick, brown paper.

Jay squeezed two tart lemons for lemonade.

Preeti ate a large, red apple.

Sumit listened to the jazz music.

## Review Work

Underline the nouns with yellow and the verbs with blue.

## Draft Book

Write five sentences that have adjectives in them. Circle the adjectives. Draw an arrow from each adjective to the noun it describes.

Name ______________________________

# Find and Circle

**adjectives**

Adjectives are words that describe nouns. Circle the adjectives.

| | | | | |
|---|---|---|---|---|
| young | held | smooth | Anna | silver |
| know | eleven | damp | cranky | grandmother |
| purple | nasty | rotten | boots | shown |
| goofy | prickly | phone | chilly | tissue |
| speedy | ripped | tight | exhausted | Bangalore |
| rectangular | dog | slept | pen | run |

**Add adjectives to finish the sentences. You may use adjectives from the word bank.**

The ______________________________ water was fun to swim in.

Mrs. Hosali carried a ______________________________ basket.

The ______________________________ owl hooted softly.

Jessie ate the ______________________________ pie.

The ______________________________ sand toasted our ______________________________ feet.

______________________________ children gathered for the ______________________________ programme.

Suma touched the ______________________________ cockroach.

The ______________________________ snake slithered across the ______________________________ pavement.

## Review Work

In the word bank, underline the nouns with yellow and the verbs with blue.

## Draft Book

Write five sentences that have adjectives in them. Circle the adjectives. Draw an arrow from each adjective to the noun it describes.

Name ______________________________

# Get the Picture

adjectives

Adjectives are words that describe nouns. They tell what kind, how many or which one.

**Write three adjectives for each noun, one adjective for each category. Do not repeat any adjectives. The first one has been done for you.**

| noun | What kind? | How many? | Which one? |
|---|---|---|---|
| gorilla | furry | few | black |
| plant | | | |
| cookie | | | |
| mansion | | | |
| costume | | | |
| planet | | | |
| volcano | | | |
| insect | | | |
| lizard | | | |

## Review Work

Choose two noun/adjective sets. Write a sentence using the words.

______________________________________________

______________________________________________

## Draft Book

Write a story using the other noun/adjective sets. Underline the nouns with yellow. Circle each adjective and draw an arrow to the noun it describes.

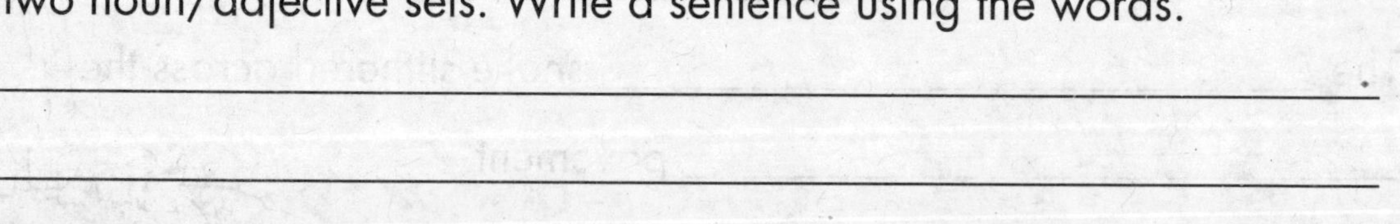

Name ______________________________

# Confusion — nouns, verbs and adjectives

Nouns are words that name people, places and things. Verbs are words that tell what someone or something is doing. Adjectives are words that describe nouns. Sometimes a word that is a noun in one sentence can be a verb or adjective in another sentence. How the word is used in a sentence determines what type of word it is.

**example:** That **fly** is bothering me. (noun)
**example:** I **fly** my kite. (verb)
**example:** Jamie caught the **fly** ball. (adjective)

**What type of word is the underlined word in each sentence? Write adjective, noun or verb on each line.**

Sam will iron his wrinkled pants. ____________________

Sheila wrinkled her nose at the nasty smell. ____________________

The ship is docked at the pier. ____________________

The Shoes Company will ship my new boots tomorrow. ____________________

Goldfish live in a liquid environment. ____________________

This liquid will pour easily. ____________________

Vimal likes the painted horse best. ____________________

Rekha painted her dresser blue. ____________________

Manu paints many things. ____________________

Nadiya bought a new set of paints. ____________________

## Review Work

Underline the verbs in the sentences with blue. Next to each sentence, write the verb tense: P = present, S = past or F = future.

## Draft Book

Think of two words that can be used as a noun and a verb. Write two sentences for each of the words. Use the words differently in each sentence.

Name ________________________________

# At the Beginning

**prefixes**

A prefix is a group of letters added to the beginning of a word. It adds meaning or changes word meaning. The word the prefix is added to is called the root, or base, word. When adding a prefix, the spelling of the root word is not changed. Some common prefixes are *re-*, *un-*, *pre-*, *dis-*, *mis-*, *bi-* and *uni-*.

**re:** again **pre:** before **un, dis, mis:** not or against **bi:** two **uni:** one

**Match the words with their meanings.**

| | |
|---|---|
| unhappy | wind again |
| bicycle | not known |
| rewind | every two months |
| uncover | cycle with one wheel |
| uninformed | not happy |
| prewritten | not cover |
| bimonthly | not informed |
| unknown | cycle with two wheels |
| unicycle | written before |

**Underline the words with prefixes in each sentence. Write the meaning of the word on the line.**

anubha's umbrella remained unopened until it began to rain

______________________________________________

lekha bought prewashed jeans

______________________________________________

gautam is going for his biweekly allergy shot

______________________________________________

## Review Work

Add uppercase letters and ending punctuation to the sentences.

## Draft Book

Make a list of words that use prefixes. Write the full word, then the prefix and base word separately. Use these words in future writing assignments.

Name ______________________________

# At the End

## suffixes *-er* and *-est*

A suffix is a group of letters added to the end of a word. It adds meaning or changes a word's meaning. The word the suffix is added to is called the root, or base, word. Most words just add endings; however, there are exceptions.

If a word ends with e, drop the e and add the ending: make - e + er = maker
If a word ends in *y*, change *y* to *i* and add the ending:
happy - y + i + er = happier
If a word ends with a short vowel with one consonant, double the consonant and add the ending: fat + t + er = fatter

Two common suffixes are *-er* and *-est*. *-Er* means more. *-Est* means most. Sometimes when *-er* is added to a verb, however, it makes a noun that means *someone who*.

**example:** A **painter** is someone who paints.

**Write the underlined base word with the correct ending.**

The animal that is the most mean is the ______________________.

The person who is the most loud is the ______________________.

Someone who is more fast is ______________________.

A person who bakes is a ______________________.

The child who is more quiet is ______________________.

A person who swims is a ______________________.

The person who is the most angry is the ______________________.

**Underline the word with a suffix. Write its meaning on the line.**

your sunglasses are darker than mine ______________________

that is the slowest horse of the bunch ______________________

that aisle is narrower than it was before ______________________

### Review Work

Add uppercase letters and add ending punctuation in the last three sentences.

### Draft Book

Write ten sentences using words with the suffixes *-er* and *-est*.

Name ________________________________

# Endings

**suffixes**

A suffix is a group of letters added to the end of a word. It adds meaning or changes a word's meaning. The word the suffix is added to is called the root, or base, word. When a suffix begins with a vowel, a change to the base word may be needed.

If a word ends with *e*, drop the *e* and add the ending: bake - e + ing = baking

If a word ends in a consonant + *y*, change *y* to *i* and add the ending (if adding *-ing*, keep the *y* and add *-ing*): carry - y + i + ed = carried
hurry + ing = hurrying

If a word ends in a vowel + *y*, add the ending: play + ing = playing

If a word has a short vowel with one consonant, double the consonant and add the ending: sun + n + y = sunny    bat + t + ed = batted

Some common suffixes that begin with vowels are: *-ed*, *-ing*, *-able*, *-er*, *-y*, and *-est*.

**Write the base word with the suffix.**

love + able = ____________________    bike + er = ____________________

carry + ing = ____________________    nice + est = ____________________

stop + ed = ____________________    scurry + ed = ____________________

fun + y = ____________________    identify + ing = ____________________

**Circle the correct spelling.**

Olive is (carriing, carrying) a large box.

Irfan (multiplyed, multiplied) the two numbers.

Jairam is (rideing, riding) his bike.

Sarah watched that (scarey, scary) movie.

## Review Work

Underline the nouns in the sentences with yellow.

## Draft Book

Make a list of words that use suffixes. Write the full word, then the suffix and base word separately. Use these words in future writing assignments.

Name ______________________

# Endings

suffixes

A suffix is a group of letters added to the end of a word. It adds meaning or changes a word's meaning. The word the suffix is added to is called the root, or base, word. When a suffix begins with a consonant, changes to the base word are usually not needed.
Some common suffixes beginning with consonants are: *-ful*, *-ly*, *-less*, and *-ness*.

**Write the base word with the suffix.**

pain + ful = ______________________

forget + ful = ______________________

forgive + ness = ______________________

fear + ful + ly = ______________________

sincere + ly = ______________________

near + ly = ______________________

fear + less = ______________________

hair + less = ______________________

care + less = ______________________

grace + ful = ______________________

sad + ness = ______________________

glad + ness = ______________________

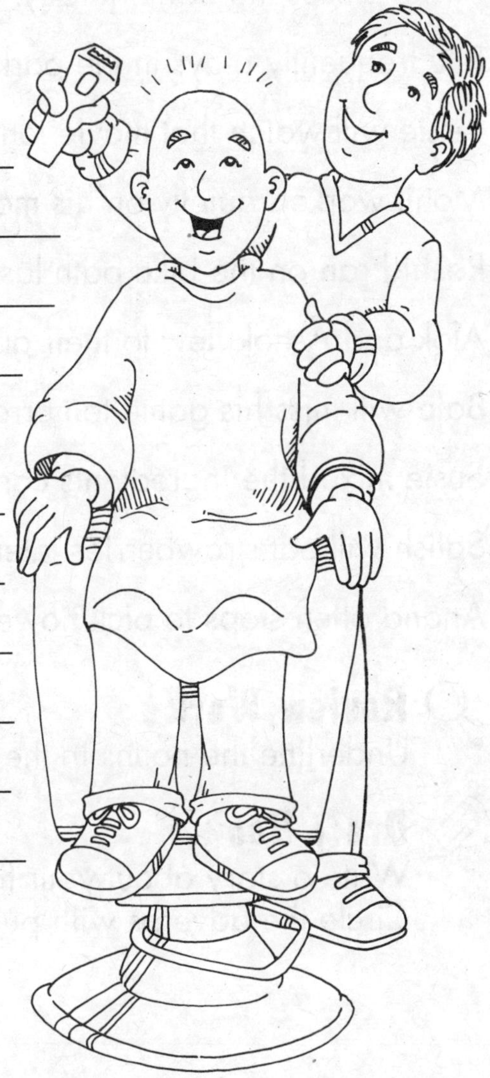

## Review Work

Write five sentences using words with suffixes. You may use some of the words listed above or choose your own.

## Draft Book

Find a page of writing in your Draft Book. Choose three words on the page that you can add suffixes to. Write the root words and the suffixes separately, then the full word. Tell what each new word means.

Name ______________________________

# How, Where or When

**adverbs**

Adverbs are words that tell more about verbs. They tell how, where or when something happens.

**Underline the verb in each sentence. Circle the adverbs that tell how, where and when.**

Nisha closes the book quickly.

Ritu frequently plays in the park.

Jessie will watch that movie tonight.

Mohit worked quietly on his model.

Rashid ran on the bike path last week.

Alok and Ashok flew to their grandma's yesterday.

Bala will miss his game tomorrow.

Susie mixed the ingredients carefully.

Satish will eat strawberries later.

Anand often stops to pick flowers.

## Review Work

Underline the nouns in the sentences with yellow.

## Draft Book

Write a story about your favourite movie. Include adverbs.
Circle the adverbs with purple.

Name ______________________________

# How Was it Done? adverbs

Adverbs are words that tell more about verbs. They tell how, where or when something happens.

**What does each adverb tell about the verb? Write *how, where* or *when* on each line. Draw an arrow to the verb the adverb is telling more about.**

Lata worked **smarter** than she had in the past. ______________

Nihar swam **through** the channel. ______________

Arti jogs **daily**. ______________

The wind **wildly** blew the branches. ______________

Rita complained **loudly**. ______________

The storm will be here **soon**. ______________

Nita **never** cheats. ______________

Suraiah **cheerfully** sets the table. ______________

Irfan **always** wears his bike helmet. ______________

Suman rubbed the wet dog **vigorously** with a towel. ______________

After playing all day, Govind went **inside** to relax. ______________

Maya put the cookies **up** on the shelf. ______________

## Review Work

Underline the nouns in the sentences with yellow.

## Draft Book

Write a story about a thunderstorm you remember. Include adverbs. Circle the adverbs with purple.

Name ______________________________

# Tell About It

**adverbs**

Adverbs are words that tell more about verbs. They tell how, where or when something happens.

**Write three adverbs for each verb, one adverb for each category. Do not repeat any adverbs.**

| verb | How? | Where? | When? |
|---|---|---|---|
| climb | | | |
| exercise | | | |
| screech | | | |
| munch | | | |
| paint | | | |
| explode | | | |
| sting | | | |
| shred | | | |

## Review Work

Choose two verb/adverbs sets. Write a sentence using each set of words. Change the tenses of the verbs if needed.

______________________________

______________________________

## Draft Book

Write a story using the other verb/adverbs sets. Underline the verbs with blue. Circle each adverb with purple and draw an arrow to the verb it describes.

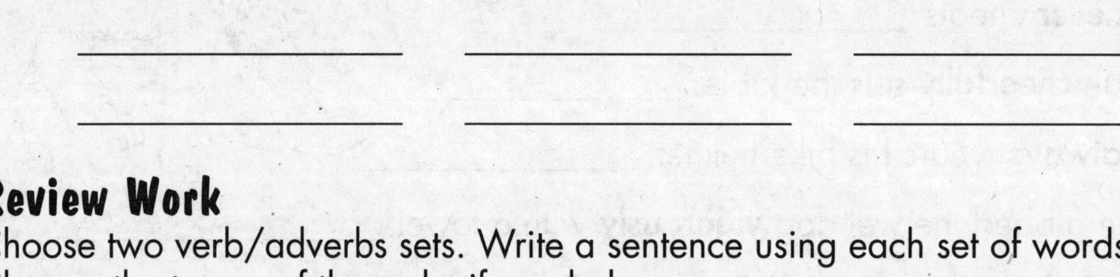

Name ______________________________

# Mathematics

## articles a, an, the

*A*, *an* and *the* are articles. An article comes before a noun or adjective/noun combination. Use *a* in front of words that start with a consonant sound. Use *an* in front of words that start with a vowel sound. Use *the* if reference is being made to a specific thing or things.

**Write *a* or *an* in front of these mathematical items.**

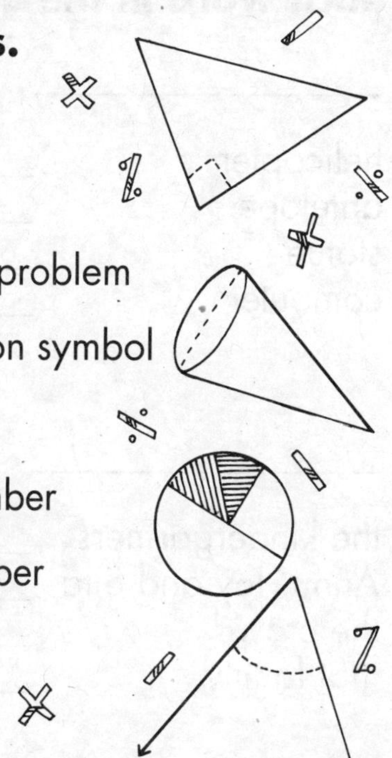

________ intersection

________ addend

________ right triangle

________ fraction

________ equal sign

________ difference

________ ordered pair

________ cone

________ multiple

________ addition problem

________ subtraction symbol

________ sum

________ even number

________ odd number

**Write *a*, *an* or *the* on the lines.**

Lillie is learning about shapes in maths. She draws ________ oval on her paper. ________ oval has no corners or sides. Next, she draws ________ octagon, which is ________ eight-sided figure. Then, Lillie draws ________ figure with ________ acute angle. Lillie enjoys drawing ________ different shapes. Now, she will colour ________ shapes with ________ marker.

### Review Work

Circle the uppercase letter at the beginning of each sentence and the ending punctuation.

### Draft Book

Find a story you have written in your Draft Book. Circle the articles in orange. If an article is incorrect, fix it.

Name ______________________

# Pick the Pronoun

## subject pronouns

A pronoun takes the place of a noun. Subject pronouns take the place of the simple subject nouns. They are: *I*, *you*, *he*, *she*, *we*, *they* and *it*.

**Above each group of words, write the pronoun that could replace each word in the group. Add four nouns to each list.**

______________

helicopter ______________
antelope ______________
statue ______________
computer ______________

______________

my sister ______________
Ms. Leela ______________
Brinda ______________
Grandma ______________

______________

the kindergartners ______________
Annu, Joy and Sita ______________
the crowd ______________
that family ______________

______________

my class and I ______________
my sister and I ______________
my team and I ______________
you and I ______________

______________

Dad ______________
my brother ______________
Mr. Nishant ______________
Alok ______________

### Review Work

Draw an X next to each proper noun.

### Draft Book

Write a story about your friends. Underline the subject pronouns with red.

Name ______________________________

# Who Did It?

**subject pronouns**

A pronoun takes the place of a noun. A subject pronoun usually comes before a verb. Subject pronouns take the place of the simple subject nouns. They are: *I*, *you*, *he*, *she*, *we*, *they* and *it*.

**Replace each noun in bold type with a subject pronoun. Write the correct pronoun on the line.**

**Dilip's sheep** produced bags of wool. ______________

**Alex** and **Anika** live in Hong Kong. ______________

**Mr. Alag** is my maths teacher. ______________

**Piyush** dove into the pool. ______________

**My bike** needs a new tyre. ______________

**Mary** won first prize. ______________

**The sun** toasted my nose. ______________

**Jyoti** caught an enormous fish. ______________

**Anna** and **I** made a castle at the beach. ______________

**Write two sentences using the pronoun *you*.**

______________________________________________________________

______________________________________________________________

**Write two sentences using the pronoun *I*.**

______________________________________________________________

______________________________________________________________

## Review Work

Underline the nouns in the sentences with yellow.

## Draft Book

Find a page of writing in your Draft Book. Change the subject nouns to subject pronouns.

Name ______________________________

# Past the Verb

**object pronouns**

An object pronoun takes the place of a noun found in the complete predicate. An object pronoun usually comes after a verb. Object pronouns are: *me*, *you*, *her*, *him*, *them*, *us* and *it*.

**Replace each noun in bold type with an object pronoun. Write the correct pronoun on the line.**

Nina lobbed **the tennis ball** to Sarah. ____________

Kavita and I told the secret to **David**. ____________

Dilip sent the package to **Rahul and Anjana**. ____________

Mrs. Menon read the book with **Veena and me**. ____________

Salman spoke on the phone with **Sanjay**. ____________

The basketball swished through **the hoop**. ____________

Malini biked to the park with **Rasika**. ____________

Ramesh handed **the salt** to Manoj. ____________

The garbage truck knocked **the garbage cans** over. ____________

Alex made a sand castle with **Rina and me**. ____________

**Write a sentence using the object pronoun *me* and one with the object pronoun *you*. Remember to place each pronoun after the verb.**

**example:** The bright sun gave me a headache.

______________________________________________________________

______________________________________________________________

## Review Work

Underline the nouns with yellow. Write the correct subject pronouns above the nouns that are before the verbs.

## Draft Book

Write a story about a book you read recently. Use subject and object pronouns in your story. Underline the pronouns with red.

Name ____________________________________

# I or Me?

**pronouns**

Pronouns take the place of nouns. Subject pronouns take the place of subject nouns. Object pronouns take the place of predicate nouns. A subject pronoun usually comes before a verb. An object pronoun usually comes after a verb.

subject pronouns: I, you, he, she, we, they, it
object pronouns: me, you, her, him, them, us, it

**Circle the correct pronoun.**

(I, Me) went to the library.

Can you come to the pool with (we, us)?

(He, Him) helped (I, me) put up the poster.

Hannah delivered the package to (they, them).

(She, Her) caught a butterfly.

(We, Us) will build a tree fort.

Did (he, him) get a turn?

Jeet threw the ball to (he, him).

Diya likes soccer, but (she, her) likes golf better.

Mr. Parashar checked out the book to (she, her).

(She, Her) will put the stamp on the envelope. Then, (she, her) will mail it.

(We, Us) went with (she, her) to the store.

## Review Work

Draw a X next to each proper noun.

## Draft Book

Find a page of writing in your Draft Book. Underline the pronouns with red. Make corrections where necessary.

Name ______________________________

# Put Yourself Last

## order with I or me

When writing about yourself and other people, put yourself last in order.

**example:** Amy and I rode our bikes. (right)
I and Amy rode our bikes. (wrong)
She gave candy to Prem and me. (right)
She gave candy to me and Prem. (wrong)

**Rewrite each sentence. Put the pronoun *I* or *me* where it belongs.**

I and Manas shot arrows at the target.

______________________________

Nilima showed the book to me and Vimal.

______________________________

I and Hanif played tag with Charu.

______________________________

I and Amit closed the gate.

______________________________

Renu recited a poem to me and Mahima.

______________________________

Vineet sang "Drum Beat" with me and Sajida.

______________________________

I, Sarla and Tony shared the four scoops of ice cream.

______________________________

### Review Work

Underline the verb in each sentence with blue.

### Draft Book

Write a story about yourself and a friend. Use the skill learned on this page.

Name ____________________________________

# My Bike Bumped His Bike

**possessive pronouns**

Possessive pronouns take the place of possessive nouns. They are: *my*, *your*, *his*, *her*, *its*, *our* and *their*. The possessive pronoun *its* does not have an apostrophe.

**Write the correct possessive pronoun on each line.**

________________________ chair bumped Anil.
Jatin's

Latika broke ________________________ glasses.
Bijoy's

Rahul borrowed ________________________ markers.
Mira's and my

We tossed ________________________ slimy bones.
the dogs'

________________________ ring is loud.
The phone's

________________________ car bumped our mailbox.
My family's

Those blueberries stained ________________________ shirts.
Tarun's and Amy's

________________________ computer downloaded that message.
Sohan's

**Write a sentence for each of the following pronouns: *my* and *your*.**

______________________________________________________________

______________________________________________________________

## Review Work

Underline the verb in each sentence with blue.

## Draft Book

Write 10 sentences using possessive pronouns.

Name ______________________________

# Mine, Ours, Theirs

**possessive pronouns**

Possessive pronouns take the place of possessive nouns. They can be used before a noun or alone. The possessive pronoun *its* does not have an apostrophe.

before a noun: my, your, his, her, its, our, their
alone: mine, yours, his, hers, its, ours, theirs

**Circle the correct pronoun.**

Jan wants (my, mine) paper.

That plant is (her, hers).

(Our, Ours) house is the white one with blue trim.

Bring (your, yours) swimsuit along.

(Their, Theirs) car was parked next to the building.

Piyush has (our, his) own paints, but he wants to borrow (her, hers).

Dad will buy me a swing set like (their, theirs).

That ice cream cone you ate was (my, mine).

We will bring (our, ours) lunches on the field trip.

(Her, Hers) scissors dropped on the floor.

That team lost their bat, so they borrowed (our, ours).

Aruna has a bike, but she wants to use (your, yours).

## Review Work

Write the verb tense beside each sentence: P = present, S = past or F = future.

## Draft Book

Write 10 sentences using possessive pronouns. Use each possessive pronoun at least once.

Name ______________________________

# Subjects

**simple subject of a sentence**

The simple subject of a sentence is the noun that the sentence is about.

**example:** Lalit's **fish** swam in the aquarium.
**example: Mount Everest** is the tallest mountain in the world.

**Circle the noun that is the subject of each sentence.**

Howrah Bridge links Howrah Station to Kolkata.

Raghu's shoelace needs to be tied.

The car needs gasoline.

The water is icy cold.

My cousin vacationed in Maldives.

Diamonds are compressed coal.

My dad mowed the lawn.

Marianas Trench is in the Pacific Ocean.

That list helps me remember things.

The baseball sailed over the fence.

Our sink is leaking and needs to be fixed.

Suraj plays tennis at Olsen Courts.

## Review Work

Draw an X next to each proper noun that names a person. Draw a triangle above each proper noun that names a place.

## Draft Book

Find a full page of writing in your Draft Book. Write an *SS* above the simple subject in each sentence.

Name ________________________

# Subject Fill In

**simple subject of a sentence**

The simple subject of a sentence is the noun that the sentence is about.

**example:** Kiran's **dog** is fluffy.
**example:** The **storm** blew the old building down.

**Add a simple subject to each sentence, using a singular or plural noun as indicated. If a proper noun is used, capitalise it.**

singular A ________________ helps people keep track of dates.
plural ________________ are fun to read.
singular A ________________ climbs trees.
plural ________________ soar through the sky.
plural ________________ go very fast.
plural ________________ are fruit.
singular My ________________ is tired.
singular ________________ likes to read.
singular A ________________ is delicious.
plural ________________ are far away.
plural ________________ drift in the water.
singular ________________ is an exciting game.

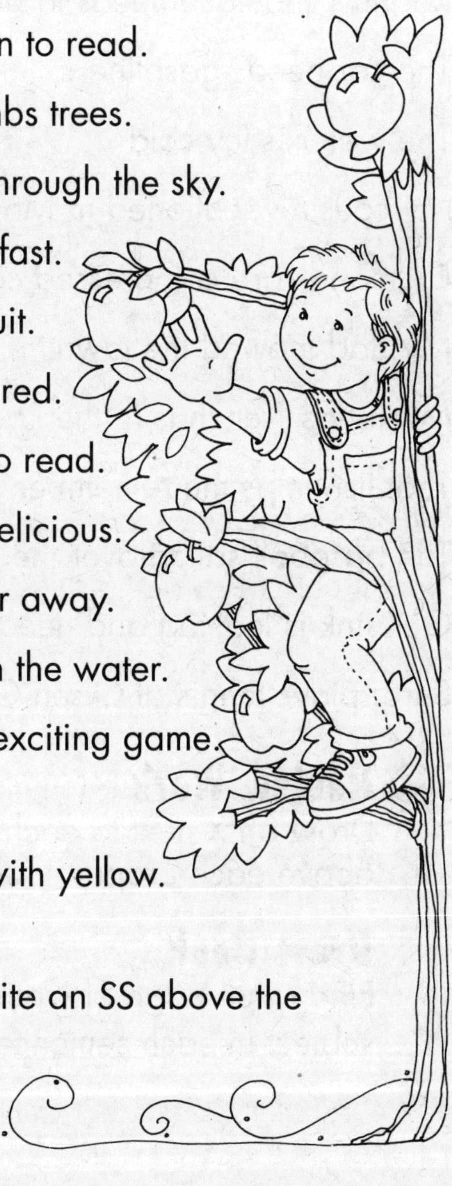

## Review Work

Underline the nouns that are not simple subjects with yellow.

## Draft Book

Find a full page of writing in your Draft Book. Write an *SS* above the simple subject in each sentence.

Name ______________________________

# Keep It Simple

**simple predicate**

The simple predicate is the verb that tells what someone or something is doing.

**example:** Imran **kicked** the football for the winning goal.

**Underline each simple predicate.**

Lina scrunched up her nose.

Deepak bounced on his bed.

Lisa rustled the bag of chips.

Anil breezed through the entryway.

The swan paddled in the pond.

The dog tripped over my foot.

Arun dated his paper.

Mrs. Tara indented the paragraph.

The pudding splattered all over the floor.

Julie scurried to get her work done.

The dancers leaped across the stage.

Manas created a new cookie.

Anil ended his story.

## Review Work

Underline the nouns with yellow.

## Draft Book

Use one sentence on this page in a story. Underline the simple predicates in your story with blue.

Name ______________________________

# Entomology

**simple subjects and predicates**

The simple predicate is the verb that tells what someone or something is doing.

**Underline each simple subject once. Underline the simple predicate twice.**

Bees buzz.

A grasshopper hops.

Butterflies migrate.

A caterpillar crawls.

A dragonfly hovers.

A hornet stings.

Ants scurry.

Silkworms spin.

Ladybugs swarm.

A cicada hums.

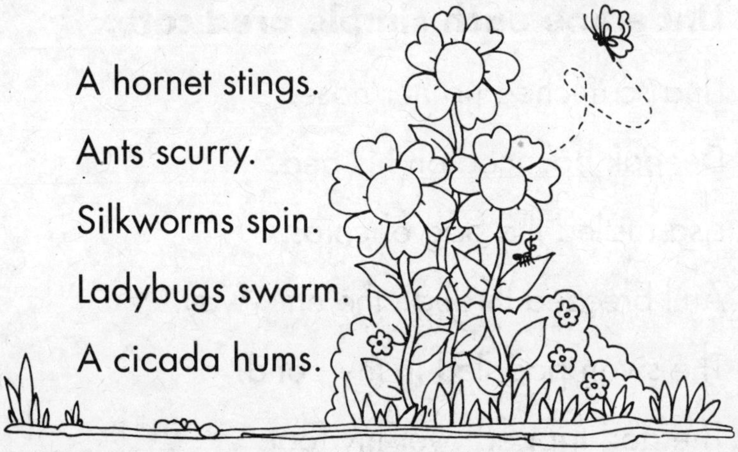

**Write the singular nouns with their verbs here.**

______________________ ______________________

______________________ ______________________

______________________

**Write the plural nouns with their verbs here.**

______________________ ______________________

______________________ ______________________

______________________

## Review Work

Choose a sentence with a singular noun. Rewrite it to make the noun plural.

______________________________________________

## Draft Book

Find a page of writing in your Draft Book. Choose five sentences from that page and rewrite them. If a noun is singular, make it plural. If a noun is plural, make it singular. Remember to change each verb, too!

Name ______________________________

# The Whole Thing

## complete subject

The simple subject is the noun that the sentence is about. The complete subject is the simple subject plus any articles or adjectives that describe or modify that noun.

**example:** The striped ball rolled down the hill.
ball = simple subject
The striped ball = complete subject
*article* *adjective*

**Circle the simple subject. Underline the complete subject.**

My third-class teacher wrote on the overhead projector.

The little, purple candy tingles on my tongue.

That enormous elephant trumpeted for an hour.

The glowing, hot lava poured down the hillside.

That skinny, black pen writes perfectly.

The noisy, bright, exciting carnival will close at 9:00.

Aruna Gopinath will throw the ball.

Her new watch broke yesterday.

The large, fierce lion cowered in the corner.

The sticky glue spilled onto Arun's pants.

### Review Work

Underline the simple predicates with blue. Write the verb tense beside each sentence: P = present, S = past and F = future.

### Draft Book

Write 10 sentences with articles or adjectives modifying the simple subjects. Circle the simple subjects and underline the complete subjects.

Name ______________________________

# Completeness

**complete subject**

The simple subject is the noun that the sentence is about. The complete subject is the simple subject plus any articles or adjectives that describe or modify that noun.

**example:** The tall oak tree swayed in the breeze.
tree = simple subject
The tall oak tree = complete subject

*article* (The) — *adjectives* (tall, oak)

Sometimes the simple subject is the complete subject.

**example:** Raj ran home.

Raj is the simple subject. Raj is also the complete subject.

**Circle the simple subject. Underline the complete subject.**

Zafar weeded the garden.

Sarika toured the village.

Vinita's little golden guinea pig ran under the dresser.

The overdone hamburgers tasted bad.

Horns blared on the street.

The recess bell rang.

Rakesh will make his bed.

An oxygen tank assists deep-sea divers.

Prickly cactus survives in hot deserts.

My ring fell into the sink.

## Review Work

Underline the simple predicates with blue. Write the verb tense beside each sentence: P = present, S = past and F = future.

## Draft Book

Write 10 sentences with articles or adjectives modifying the simple subjects. Circle the simple subjects and underline the complete subjects.

Name ______________________________

# That One

**complete subject**

The complete subject is the simple subject plus any articles or adjectives that describe or modify that noun. It can also include other modifiers you have not yet learned to identify.

**example:** The (cup) of hot chocolate is empty.

The (monkey) by the feeding bowl threw a banana.

The (apple) with a bruise fell on the floor.

**Circle the simple subject. Underline the complete subject.**

That puppy by the bench dug this big hole.

The snorkelling group of 15 swam near the reef.

Flowers from that garden smell wonderful.

The canoe alongside the dock took me to the island.

The parrot with a green head will belong to Apu when he pays for it.

The brown horse brushed my shoulder with her nose.

The slimy earthworms in that pile of leaves are great fish bait.

The mouldy bread in the garbage looks awful.

Frogs will swim in this pond when it's warmer.

That candle on the table burns brightly.

## Review Work

Underline the simple predicates with blue. Write the verb tense beside each sentence: P = present, S = past and F = future.

## Draft Book

Write 10 sentences. Circle the simple subjects and underline the complete subjects.

Name ______________________________

# Here We Go

**complete predicate**

The simple predicate is the verb that tells what someone or something is doing. The complete predicate is the simple predicate plus any helping or linking verbs and any adverbs that describe or modify the verb.

**example:** The ball will roll smoothly.
roll = simple predicate
will roll smoothly = complete predicate

*helping verb* (will) *adverb* (smoothly)

**Circle the simple predicate. Underline the complete predicate twice.**

Sanat often reads quickly.

The snow frequently fell rapidly.

The rain pounded loudly last night.

The wet dog shook vigorously.

An ant may have wandered around yesterday.

Nikhil never screams loudly.

That koala will eat constantly.

That lion could lunge immediately.

Lina may finish tonight.

Those tennis shoes smell awful.

## Review Work

Identify the verb tense of each sentence. Write the verb tense beside each sentence: P = present, S = past and F = future.

## Draft Book

Write 10 sentences with helping or linking verbs and adverbs modifying the simple predicates. Circle the simple predicates and underline the complete predicates twice.

Name ___________________________

# The Whole

## complete predicate

The complete predicate is the simple predicate plus any helping or linking verbs, any adverbs, and any other words that tell where, when, why or how the verb happens. If the words are not part of the complete subject, they are included in the complete predicate.

**example:** Sujit will bike to the beach.

The big red apple fell to the ground.

Sana played with her brother.

**Circle the simple predicate. Underline the complete predicate twice.**

The glass of milk spilled onto Hira's shoes.

Five tiny owlets hooted softly for a meal.

Chandu and Anita guarded the soccer goals.

Amrit filled the bird feeder last week.

The raccoons destroyed the garden.

The hen will gobble up any feed it finds.

Ziyad wandered aimlessly through the toy store.

Niraj quickly subtracted a page of numbers.

Roshan carefully sewed the button on his jacket.

Our family will attend the play next Tuesday.

A spider dangled above our heads.

### Review Work

Identify the verb tense of each sentence. Write the verb tense beside each sentence: P = present, S = past and F = future.

### Draft Book

Write 10 sentences with helping or linking verbs and adverbs modifying the simple predicates. Circle the simple predicates and underline the complete predicates twice.

Name ___________________________________

# Do Tell

**complete subjects and predicates**

The complete subject tells who or what the sentence is about. The complete predicate tells what the someone or something is doing.

**Underline the complete subject once. Underline the complete predicate twice.**

The noisy movie prevented Udip from working.

The box of tissues emptied quickly.

The old, rusty swing continues to be the kids' favourite.

Pradeep loads the back of the truck with plants.

Many shiny marbles scattered across the tile floor.

Many important men signed the Declaration of Independence.

Few tomato plants survived the dog's digging.

The steep cliff towered above the river.

The remote-controlled car raced along the pavement.

The giant toad devoured many insects.

The tape secured the picture to the wall.

## Review Work

Write an *SS* above the simple subject in each sentence. Circle the simple predicates.

## Draft Book

Locate a page of writing in your Draft Book. Underline each complete subject once. Underline each complete predicate twice.

Name ______________________________

# Star or X

## complete sentences

A sentence needs one complete subject and one complete predicate to be a sentence.

**example:** Jan has a dog. = sentence

complete subject   complete predicate

a dog = not a sentence

A sentence can be long or short.

**example:** Jan walks.

*complete subject*   *complete predicate*

**example:** The tiny little bird with the broken wing ← *complete subject*
finally flew out the door and into the backyard. ← *complete predicate*

**If the group of words is a sentence, put a star in the box. Underline the complete subject once. Underline the complete predicate twice. If the group of words is not a sentence, put an X in the box.**

| | |
|---|---|
| ☐ The old yellow lion in the cage. | ☐ Carrots are healthy. |
| ☐ Walking through the quiet hallway. | ☐ That butterfly is beautiful. |
| ☐ Many little. | ☐ Jay closed it. |
| ☐ The strawberries are tasty. | ☐ Jessie walks to school. |
| ☐ Are very large. | ☐ Going here? |
| ☐ In that really scary house. | ☐ The woods are. |
| ☐ Camp is fun. | ☐ This bubble gum. |

### Review Work

Write the linking verbs used in the groups of words from above.

______________________________________________

### Draft Book

Make complete sentences using each group of words that has an X in the box.

Name ______________________________

# Make the Fix

## complete sentences

A sentence needs one complete subject and one complete predicate to be a sentence.

**example:** Jan has a dog. = sentence

*complete subject* *complete predicate*

a dog = not a sentence

**These groups of words are not sentences. Rewrite them as complete sentences. Put an uppercase letter at the beginning and correct punctuation at the end.**

gallops towards

______________________________

should George

______________________________

gather those

______________________________

Uday's lizard

______________________________

ends at noon

______________________________

the enormous

______________________________

is incredible

______________________________

### Review Work

Underline each complete subject once and each complete predicate twice.

### Draft Book

Find a full page of writing in your Draft Book. Circle any groups of words that are not complete sentences and rewrite them so that they are complete.

Name ______________________________

# Is it Complete? complete sentences

A group of words needs one complete subject and one complete predicate to be a sentence.

**If the group of words is a sentence, put a star in the box. Underline the complete subject once and the complete predicate twice. If the group of words is not a sentence, put an X in the box.**

The elephant is charging ☐

Raji has three adorable kittens ☐

John coloured the frog green ☐

That pair of scissors is sharp ☐

Did Sam collect the money ☐

Should this bike ☐

Can Renuka go swimming ☐

Of red and blue paper ☐

Moaning and groaning ☐

The bluebird swooped down to grab an insect ☐

Will bats fly in the backyard tonight ☐

Prem's umbrella in the old bucket ☐

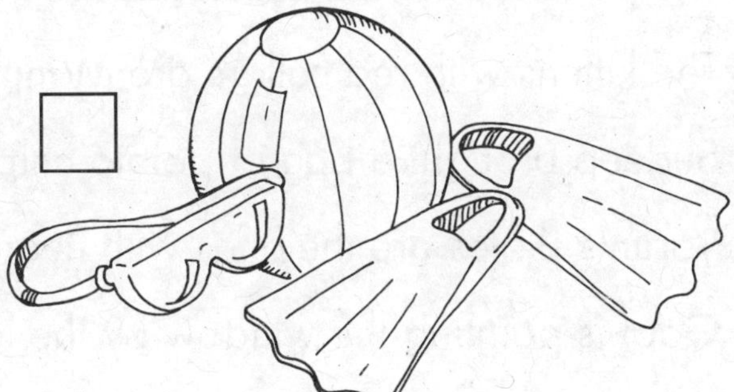

## Review Work

Write a complete sentence with each phrase with an X in its box.

## Draft Book

Find a full page of writing in your Draft Book. Circle any groups of words that are not complete sentences and rewrite them so that they are complete.

Name ___________________________

# Noun Modifiers

## prepositions

A preposition is a word that relates a noun to other words in the sentence. It can give more information as well as tell location (where a noun is), direction (where a noun is going) or time (when a noun happens). Some common prepositions are: *by*, *from*, *to*, *in*, *in front of*, *next to*, *of*, *under* and *with*. The preposition must modify, or give more information about, the noun in the sentence, not the verb.

**Circle the prepositions. Underline the nouns they are modifying.**

Madhu would like a cup of hot chocolate.

The car next to the restaurant is ours.

Fida found her pencil under the couch.

The cookies in the jar are delicious.

The letter from my grandma came last night.

The seat in the middle is John's.

Keerti bought the goldfish with five black spots.

The bump in front of your sled will send you sailing.

The paper under the couch needs to be picked up.

The kittens with red collars are Manju's.

Sudeep brought a bag of potato chips.

Varun's skates are the ones with fluorescent orange wheels.

Gopi is painting the window by the ladder.

Manohar wants a piece of pie.

### Review Work

Underline the verbs in the sentences with blue.

### Draft Book

Write a sentence for each preposition above.

Name ______________________________

# Tell Me Which One — prepositions

A preposition is a word that relates a noun to other words in the sentence. It can give more information as well as tell location (where a noun is), direction (where a noun is going) or time (when a noun happens). A preposition begins a phrase called a prepositional phrase.

noun modified

Megha drinks a cup (of) warm tea.

preposition    prepositional phrase

Prepositions include: *by*, *from*, *to*, *in*, *in front of*, *next to*, *of*, *under* and *with*. The preposition must modify, or give more information about, the noun in the sentence, not the verb.

**Circle the preposition. Underline the prepositional phrase. Draw an arrow to the noun it modifies.**

The sweater with red stripes must be washed.

The student in the blue jacket is Pranesh.

Please get the pencil by the book.

The bats in the attic are sleeping.

The sandwich in that bag is mouldy.

Malati bought a doll with brown hair.

Farhan read a chapter from that book.

That desk next to mine is messy.

Check the atlas in the bookcase.

The bowl with cereal in it fell off the counter.

### Review Work
Underline the verbs in the sentences with blue.

### Draft Book
Write a sentence for each preposition above.

Name ______________________________

# We Sound the Same homophones

Homophones are words that sound alike but are spelt differently and have different meanings.

**Write the correct homophone on the line.**

**threw:** verb, past tense of throw **through:** between, from one side to another

Ria walked ______________________________ the door.

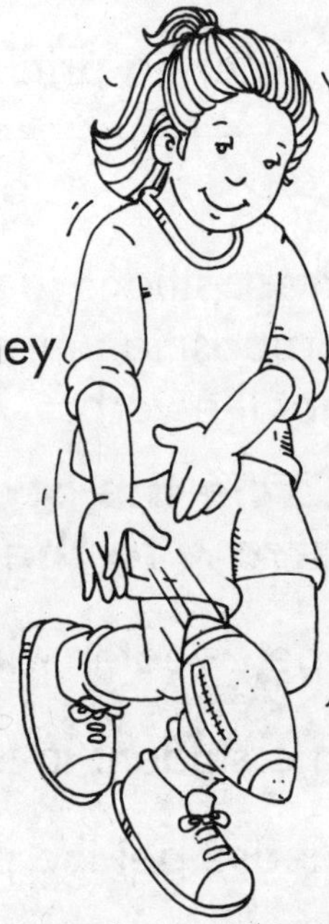

Purnima looked ______________________________ the window.

Anjali ______________________________ the winning pass.

**sent:** verb, past tense of send **scent:** a smell **cent:** unit of money

The ______________________________ of that flower is faint.

Mr. Hari ______________________________ Anila to the office.

This penny is worth one ______________________________ .

**its:** possessive pronoun **it's:** contraction for it is

______________________________ very hot outside.

The class has ______________________________ own drinking fountain.

Mrinal thinks ______________________________ too cold to go in the pool.

______________________________ place is on that shelf.

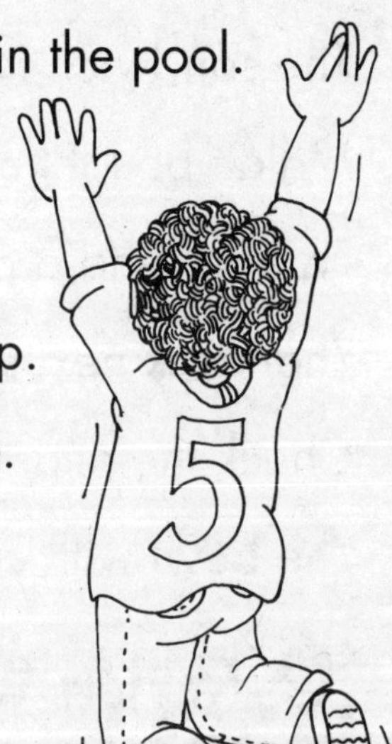

**whole:** entire **hole:** part missing

The ______________________________ class is going on a field trip.

Charumati wanted the ______________________________ apple.

There is a ______________________________ in this sock.

## Review Work

Underline the nouns with yellow.

## Draft Book

Choose a pair of homophones. Write two sentences with each word.

Name ______________________________

# We Sound the Same — homophones

Homophones are words that sound alike but are spelt differently and have different meanings.

**Write the correct homophone on the line.**

**no:** antonym of yes **know:** verb, to understand

______________________________ , you may not have any candy before dinner.

I don't ______________________________ what street Priyesh lives on.

There are ______________________________ dogs allowed here.

**new:** not old **knew:** verb, past tense of know

Jafar has a ______________________________ bike.

Nilima ______________________________ where Rakhi lived.

The ______________________________ theatre has comfortable seats.

**write:** verb, to make purposeful marks, for example with a pencil
**right:** to be correct or a direction opposite of left

Put your name in the upper ______________________________ corner.

Please ______________________________ your name on the paper.

Yes, that answer is ______________________________.

**allowed:** permitted **aloud:** out loud

We are not ______________________________ to chew gum in school.

When you read ______________________________, it bothers me.

Are we ______________________________ to bring pets to school?

## Review Work

Underline the subject pronouns, object pronouns and possessive pronouns with red.

## Draft Book

Choose one pair of homophones. Write two sentences with each word.

Name ______________________________

# We Sound the Same — homophones

Homophones are words that sound alike but are spelt differently and have different meanings.

**Write the correct homophone on the line.**

**here:** location word **hear:** to understand sound by way of the ear

Did you ______________________________ the owl hooting last night?

They were ______________________________ last night.

You can sit ______________________________ beside me.

Sorry, I couldn't ______________________________ you.

**by:** near **buy:** to purchase

Put the pencil ______________________________ the stack of books.

I would like to ______________________________ that toy.

Where can I ______________________________ new shoes?

Karuna is standing ______________________________ the water fountain.

**there:** location word **their:** possessive pronoun **they're:** contraction for they are

Would you put this paper over ______________________________ ?

He will go ______________________________ for vacation.

Do you think ______________________________ mother likes snakes?

______________________________ bringing a snake home.

I think ______________________________ still in gym.

### Review Work

Underline the subject pronouns, object pronouns and possessive pronouns with red.

### Draft Book

Choose one pair of homophones. Write two sentences with each word.

Name ______________________________

# To, Too, Two

**homophones**

To, too, and two are homophones.

**to** is used in place of toward or with a verb: Rita went **to** school.
I like **to** eat candy.

**two** is a number word for the numeral 2: Irfan has **two** sisters.

**too** means also or more than enough: Uday wants some milk, **too**.
That music is **too** noisy.

**Write *to, too* or *two* on each line.**

tanya left at ________________ o'clock

is that soup ________________ hot

are you tired, ________________

________________ lions roared

my aunt plans ________________ come ________________ our football

game, ________________

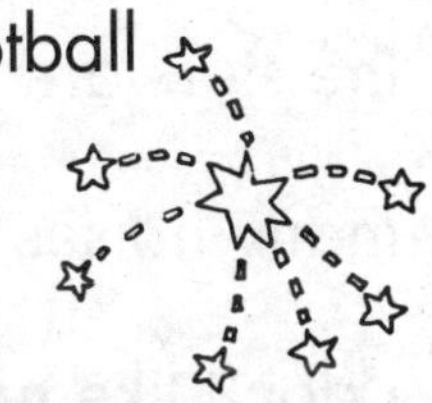

you can have ________________ stickers, ________________

tina went ________________ ________________ amusement parks this summer

anant broke ________________ crayons

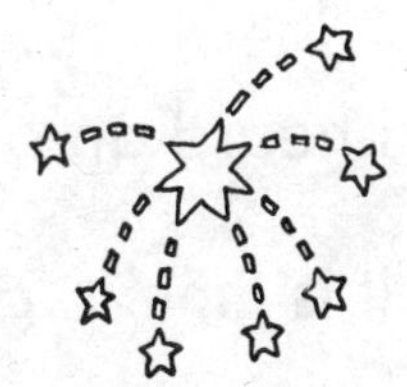

we saw ________________ hours of fireworks

anjali threw the ball ________________ arun

please give those ________________ crickets ________________ george

sheila will mail the letter ________________ alia

## Review Work

Add uppercase letters and ending punctuation.

## Draft Book

Write three sentences with each meaning of these homophones.

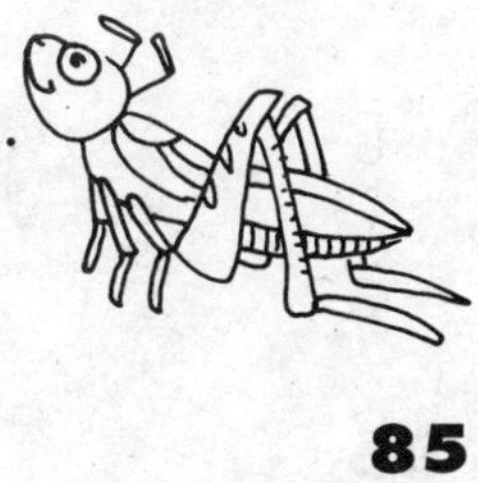

Name ______________________________

# Evening

**declarative sentences**

A declarative sentence tells something. It begins with an uppercase letter and ends with a full stop.

**Cross out the first letter of each sentence and write the uppercase letter next to it. Put a full stop at the end of each sentence.**

the sky is beginning to darken ☐

a shooting star streaked across the sky ☐

i wonder how far away the nearest star is ☐

haley looked at stars through the telescope ☐

dev saw Jupiter and Venus last night ☐

the stars are not as bright as the moon ☐

many noises can be heard at night ☐

i don't like night noises that are scary ☐

the full moon is rising above the trees ☐

i heard an owl hoot ☐

it is time to go to bed ☐

## Review Work

Circle the adjectives with orange.

## Draft Book

Write six interrogative and six declarative sentences. Begin each sentence with an uppercase letter and end it with the correct punctuation mark.

Name ______________________________

# I Want to Know

**interrogative sentences**

An interrogative sentence asks a question. It begins with an uppercase letter and ends with a question mark.

**Rewrite each interrogative sentence. Put an uppercase letter at the beginning and a question mark at the end.**

who owns that red bike

______________________________

what kind of insect is that

______________________________

how did the kite get stuck in that tree

______________________________

where do fruit bats sleep

______________________________

who was emperor Ashoka

______________________________

did it rain in Bangalore

______________________________

will you turn off that loud music

______________________________

are those cookies still hot

______________________________

## Review Work

Some of the sentences above have linking or helping verbs. Underline these verbs with blue.

## Draft Book

Write five interrogative sentences. Begin each sentence with an uppercase letter and end it with a question mark.

Name ______________________________

# Where?

**declarative and interrogative sentences**

A declarative sentence tells something and ends with a full stop. An interrogative sentence asks a question and ends with a question mark.

**Put the correct punctuation mark at the end of each sentence. Answer the question with a declarative sentence using the information given.**

Kangaroos live where koalas live ☐ Koalas live in Australia ☐

Where do kangaroos live ☐

______________________________________________

Wild penguins do not live north of the equator ☐ Alaska is north of the equator ☐

Do wild penguins live in Alaska ☐

______________________________________________

Monarch butterflies migrate to Michigan in the spring ☐ These butterflies migrate to Mexico in the fall ☐ Are monarchs in Michigan in winter ☐

______________________________________________

Orangutans live in a small part of Southeast Asia ☐ The Brazilian rain forest is in South America ☐ Do orangutans live in the Brazilian rain forest ☐

______________________________________________

## Review Work

Choose one declarative sentence from each group of sentences. Underline the complete subject once. Underline the complete predicate twice.

## Draft Book

Write your own set of interrogative and declarative sentences. Begin each sentence with an uppercase letter and end it with the correct punctuation mark.

Name ______________________________

# Wow!

## exclamatory sentences

An exclamatory sentence shows strong feelings and ends with an exclamation mark.

**Rewrite each exclamatory sentence. Put uppercase letters where they belong and exclamation marks at the ends.**

this dessert is delicious

______________________________

that comet is breathtaking

______________________________

we're going to bangalore

______________________________

ouch, get off my foot

______________________________

you startled me

______________________________

the fireworks are incredible

______________________________

i did not crack that plate

______________________________

### Review Work

Choose one sentence from above and draw a star next to it. Pretend that sentence is the answer and write a question for it.

______________________________

### Draft Book

Write five exclamatory sentences. Begin each sentence with an uppercase letter and end it with an exclamation mark.

Name ______________________________

# Amusement Park

## declarative, interrogative and exclamatory sentences

A declarative sentence tells something and ends with a full stop. An interrogative sentence asks a question and ends with a question mark. An exclamatory sentence shows strong feelings and ends with an exclamation mark.

**Put the correct punctuation mark at the end of each sentence. Write *declarative, interrogative* or *exclamatory* on the line.**

our class is going to the amusement park ☐ ______________________

the bus will leave early ☐ ______________________

did you set your alarm clock ☐ ______________________

abu and i stood in line together ☐ ______________________

yikes, the food here is expensive ☐ ______________________

did you bring lunch ☐ ______________________

i'm glad i did ☐ ______________________

we put our lunches into lockers ☐ ______________________

let's go to the rides ☐ ______________________

mona, julie, manas and i get in line for a roller coaster ☐ ______________________

we put on our seat belts and harnesses ☐ ______________________

i'm scared ☐ ______________________

### Review Work

Review the sentence for words that should start with uppercase letters. Cross out the lowercase letters and write the uppercase letters above them.

### Draft Book

Write three declarative, three interrogative and three exclamatory sentences. Begin each sentence with an uppercase letter and end it with the correct punctuation mark.

Name ________________________________

# Now Do This

## imperative sentences

A sentence that tells you what to do or gives you a command is called an imperative sentence. An imperative sentence usually ends with a full stop.

**Rewrite these imperative sentences. Put an uppercase letter at the beginning of each sentence and a full stop at the end.**

buckle your seat belt

______________________________________________

obey traffic signals

______________________________________________

put on your helmet before riding your bike

______________________________________________

start all sentences with uppercase letters

______________________________________________

turn off those lights

______________________________________________

always capitalise proper nouns

______________________________________________

finish your work

______________________________________________

put a full stop at the end of a declarative sentence

______________________________________________

### Review Work

Underline the verbs in the sentences with blue.

### Draft Book

Write five imperative sentences. Begin each sentence with an uppercase letter and end it with a full stop.

Name ______________________________

# With Feeling

## imperative sentences

A sentence that tells you what to do or gives you a command is called an imperative sentence. Most imperative sentences end with full stops. Occasionally, a command is given with great feeling. In this case, an exclamation mark is used. The same command can end with either a full stop or an exclamation mark depending on the situation.

**example:** Sit down. → Mom is asking you to sit down to dinner.
Sit down! → A small child is standing on a rocking chair, and it is about to tip over.

**Read the situation. Put the correct punctuation at the end of each imperative sentence.**

Don't touch that ☐ The burner was just turned off and is still extremely hot.

Don't touch that ☐ Dad put a bowl of carrots on the table for dinner.

Hold still ☐ Five hornets are flying around.

Hold still ☐ Samir is tying his brother's shoe.

Come here ☐ Your dog tries to wander into the woods at night.

Come here ☐ Anup wants to tell Moti something.

Shut the gate ☐ Nandu left the gate open.

Shut the gate ☐ The neighbour's dog is coming.

Stop that ☐ Ann tapped her brother on the shoulder.

Stop that ☐ Ann's little brother is trying to light matches.

### Review Work
Underline the verbs in the sentences with blue.

### Draft Book
Write eight imperative sentences. Begin each sentence with an uppercase letter. End some of the sentences with full stops and some with exclamation marks. Describe each situation where you use an exclamation mark.

Name ____________________________________

# You, That's Who

## subject of imperative sentences

A sentence that tells you what to do or gives you a command is called an imperative sentence. An imperative sentence usually ends with a full stop. An imperative sentence looks like a complete predicate. The complete subject is *you*. *You* is implied, which means that since the speaker is talking to you, it is understood that *you* is the subject even though the word *you* isn't written.

**Underline the complete predicate twice. Circle the simple predicate. Remember that in each sentence, the subject is *you*.**

Run to the mailbox and get the mail.

Always capitalise the word "I."

Put the blanket over the birdcage.

Swat the mosquito above your head.

Get into bed immediately.

Don't spill juice on the carpet.

Brush your teeth every morning and night.

Write Grandma a thank-you note tonight.

Hold the ladder while I wash the window.

Stick the stamp on the corner of the envelope.

Please work quietly.

Ride slowly down that steep hill.

### Review Work

Circle the adverbs with purple.

### Draft Book

Write 10 imperative sentences. Begin each sentence with an uppercase letter and end it with a full stop.

Name ______________________________

# Hiding Adjectives

**predicate adjectives**

Adjectives describe nouns. Predicates refer to verbs. A predicate adjective is an adjective that follows a linking verb. It is part of the complete predicate but it describes the simple subject.

**example:** The monster was gigantic.

**Circle the predicate adjectives. Draw an arrow from each adjective to the noun it describes.**

This cave is scary.

Salma is helpful.

That huge tractor is muddy.

The three children were tired.

Ann was angry.

The dough is squishy.

The trailer was empty.

The class has been quiet.

That towering cliff is beautiful!

That assignment was difficult.

The new tape is sticky.

## Review Work

Underline each complete subject once and each complete predicate twice.

## Draft Book

Write 10 sentences that use predicate adjectives. Underline each predicate adjective and draw an arrow to the noun it describes. Underline the linking verbs with blue. Begin each sentence with an uppercase letter.

Name ______________________________

# It Was Done to Whom?

**direct objects**

A direct object is the noun that receives the action of the verb. It is located in the complete predicate. To locate the direct object, find the verb. Find a noun after the verb. If the verb is acting on the noun, the noun is the direct object.

**example:** The ball hit Mala.

*verb* (hit) *noun* (Mala)

Mala is the direct object because the ball hit or acted on her.

**example:** I sent David some money.

*verb* (sent) *nouns* (David, money)

Money is the direct object because the money was sent, not David.

**Circle the verb. Draw an arrow to the direct object it affects.**

The crab snapped his claws at the fish.

The starfish ate the clam.

The window air conditioner cooled the room.

The whale's tail smacked the water.

Five red ants carried off that beetle.

Lyla threw the markers across the table.

The dolphin can locate food with sonar.

Over time, coral builds islands.

The floating jellyfish stung the swimmer.

Wahid rode his bike down the road.

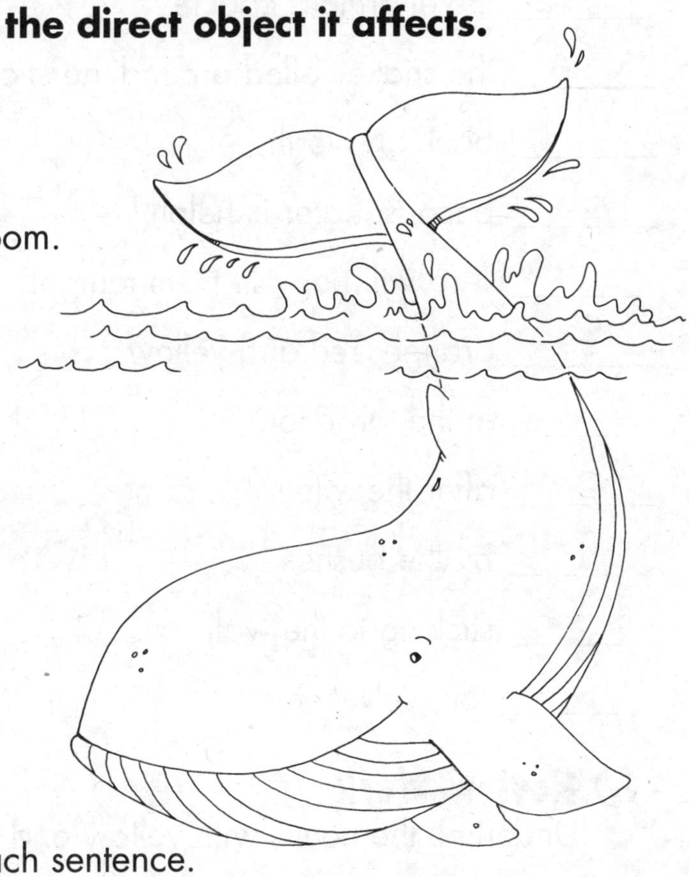

## Review Work

Underline the complete subject of each sentence.

## Draft Book

Write four sentences using direct objects. Underline the direct object in each sentence with green.

Name ______________________________

# Just a Piece

**phrases and clauses**

A phrase is a group of words that does not have a subject and predicate. A clause is a group of words with a subject and a predicate. An independent clause can stand alone as a sentence. A dependent clause cannot stand alone as a sentence.

**Write *P* if the group of words is a phrase. Write *IC* if the group of words is an independent clause. Add uppercase letters and punctuation, if needed. Write *DC* if the group of words is a dependent clause.**

________ Uday has the flu

________ whenever you can

________ the enormous cookie

________ the snake coiled around the stick

________ back and forth

________ because Jafar is helpful

________ Tara will baby-sit them tonight

________ orange, red and yellow

________ in the large jar

________ after the rain stops

________ by the bushes

________ sticking to the wall

________ soft, velvety fur

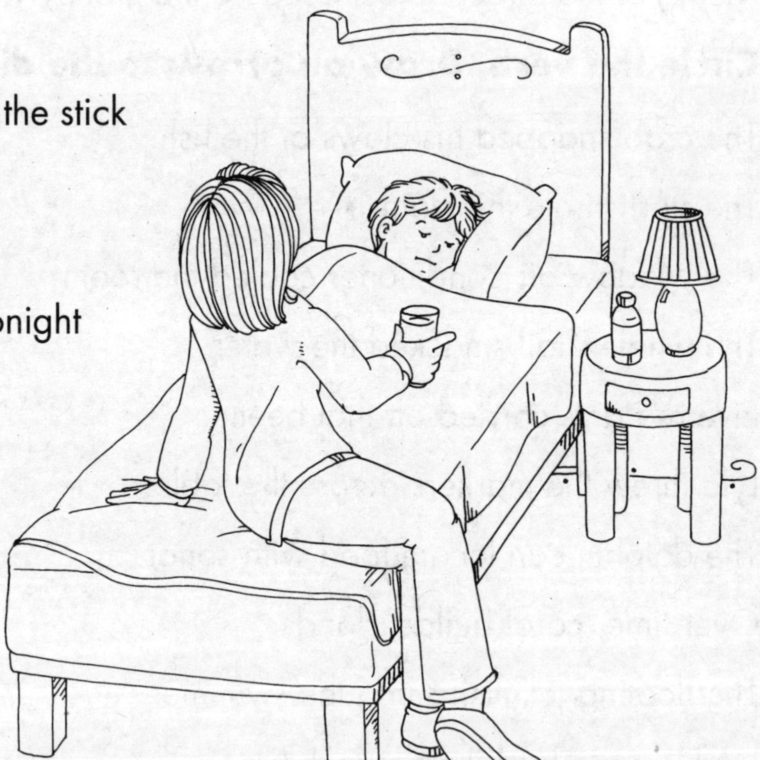

## Review Work

Underline the nouns with yellow and the verbs with blue.

## Draft Book

Use the phrases and dependent clauses to write complete sentences.

Name ______________________________

# Combining Sentences

**coordinating conjunctions**

Sentences can be combined when their ideas are the same. Related sentences can be joined with coordinating conjunctions. There are seven coordinating conjunctions: *and*, *nor*, *but*, *for*, *yet*, *so* and *or*.

**examples:** Kim eats her sandwich. + Kim eats her grapes. =
Kim eats her sandwich and her grapes.

Kim eats her sandwich. + Kim did not eat her grapes. =
Kim eats her sandwich but not her grapes.

**Combine these sets of sentences. Write the new sentences on the lines.**

Anika slept on the plane. Anika did not sleep on the train.

______________________________________________

Megha played with Madhu. Megha played with Jatin.

______________________________________________

The pencil isn't new. The eraser isn't new.

______________________________________________

Ayan plays tennis. Ayan plays basketball.

______________________________________________

Sundar likes strawberries. Sundar does not like blueberries.

______________________________________________

The bat pup is soft. The bat pup is fuzzy.

______________________________________________

Pramod finished his maths. Pramod did not finish his reading.

______________________________________________

**Review Work**

Underline the complete subjects once and the complete predicates twice.

**Draft Book**

Write three pairs of sentences that can be combined. Write a combined sentence for each pair.

Name ________________________________

# Put Them Together

**combining sentences**

Sentences can be combined when their ideas are the same. Related sentences can be joined with coordinating conjunctions. There are seven coordinating conjunctions: *and*, *nor*, *but*, *for*, *yet*, *so* and *or*.

Subjects can be combined to create a compound subject.

**example:** Megha jumped on the trampoline. + Pal jumped on the trampoline. = Megha and Pal jumped on the trampoline.

Megha jumped on the trampoline. + Pal did not jump on the trampoline. = Megha but not Pal jumped on the trampoline.

**Use conjunctions to combine these sentences. Write the new sentences on the lines.**

Ants live in communities. Bees live in communities.

________________________________

Penguins live in Antarctica. Polar bears do not live in Antarctica.

________________________________

Alice climbed the stairs. Ria climbed the stairs.

________________________________

Paul read that book. Mary did not read that book.

________________________________

The little grey duck swam in the pond. The baby swan swam in the pond.

________________________________

Starfish live in the ocean. Anemones live in the ocean.

________________________________

## Review Work

Underline the complete subjects once and the complete predicates twice.

## Draft Book

Write five sets of sentences whose subjects can be combined. Trade with a partner and combine the sentences.

Name ____________________

# Doing Many Things

**combining sentences**

Sentences can be combined when their ideas are the same. Related sentences can be joined with coordinating conjunctions. There are seven coordinating conjunctions: *and*, *nor*, *but*, *for*, *yet*, *so* and *or*.

Verbs can be combined to create a compound predicate.

**example:** Jay planted the seeds. + Jay watered the seeds. =
Jay planted and watered the seeds.

**Use conjunctions to combine these sentences. Write the new sentences on the lines.**

Hira weeded the garden. Hira watered the garden.

_______________________________________________

The bird caught insects. The bird ate insects.

_______________________________________________

Rina slipped on the ice. Rina fell on the ice.

_______________________________________________

The snake slid through the grass. The snake slithered through the grass.

_______________________________________________

The chocolate was warmed. The chocolate was melted.

_______________________________________________

Nyla hangs the picture. Nyla straightens the picture.

_______________________________________________

Irfan filled the water balloon. Irfan threw the water balloon.

_______________________________________________

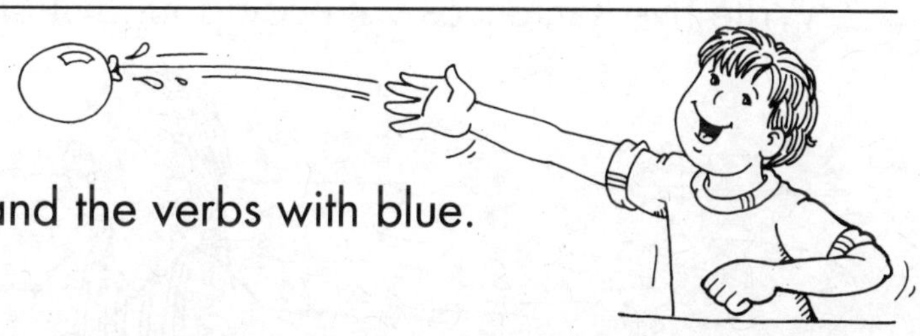

## Review Work

Underline the nouns with yellow and the verbs with blue.

## Draft Book

Write five pairs of sentences whose predicates can be combined. Write a combined sentence for each pair.

Name ________________________________

# And, And, And

## combining sentences

Sentences can be combined when their ideas are the same. Related sentences can be joined with coordinating conjunctions. There are seven coordinating conjunctions: *and*, *nor*, *but*, *for*, *yet*, *so* and *or*.

**Circle the coordinating conjunctions. If the sentence has a compound subject, write *CS*. If the sentence has a compound predicate, write *CP*. If it has both, write *B*.**

________ Joy and Smita walk in the parade.

________ Rohan grabbed and climbed the rope.

________ The monkey hit the window and pounded on the wall.

________ The thief grabbed her purse and ran for the door.

________ The carpet and the couch need cleaning.

________ The ants and beetles scurried and hid.

________ Mia grabs the door and slams it.

________ Candies and peanuts fell on the floor and rolled around.

________ Your bedroom and the living room are messy.

________ Mala and Rita swim and dive in the lake.

### Review Work

Underline the simple subjects with yellow and simple predicates with blue.

### Draft Book

Write five sentences with compound subjects, compound predicates or both.

Name ________________________________

# Check the Verb

**combining sentences, subject-verb agreement**

Sentences can be combined when their ideas are the same. Sometimes the verb must be changed when the subject changes from singular to plural.

**example:** Jan <u>likes</u> milk. + Tom <u>likes</u> milk. = Jan and Tom <u>like</u> milk.

**Put a box around each conjunction. Circle the correct verb.**

The teddy bear and the doll (sit, sits) on her pillow.

Rita and Lina (slide, slides) down the twisty slide.

The lion and tiger (is, are) pacing in their cages.

The grey car and the white van (was, were) washed today.

That large horsefly and this buzzing mosquito (fly, flies) through the open door.

The large snail and that orange and black goldfish (live, lives) in this aquarium.

The hot tub and the pool (is, are) empty.

Rohit and Ganesh (enjoy, enjoys) music with a fast beat.

Juicy hot dogs and puffy, white marshmallows (toast, toasts) over the campfire.

My blue pajamas and fuzzy slippers (is, are) packed.

## Review Work

Underline the nouns with yellow. Draw an arrow from each adjective to the noun it describes.

## Draft Book

Write five sets of sentences whose subjects can be combined. Trade with a partner and combine the sentences. Watch subject-verb agreement!

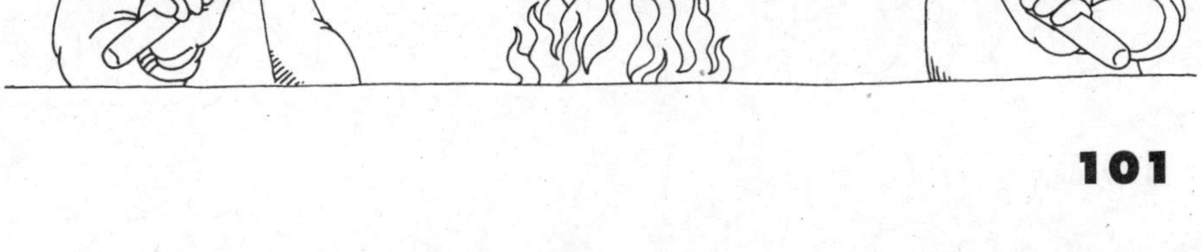

Name ______________________________

# No Run-Ons

**independent clauses and conjunctions**

When two independent clauses are written together, they create a run-on sentence. Two related independent clauses can be joined into one sentence with a coordinating conjunction. There are seven coordinating conjunctions: *and*, *nor*, *but*, *for*, *yet*, *so* and *or*. A comma and a conjunction are needed to join two independent clauses into one sentence to avoid a run-on.

**example:** Jasmin needs a nap, or she may fall asleep.

*subject predicate conjunction subject predicate*

**Circle each comma and coordinating conjunction.**

Hanif likes art, but he likes maths better.

Soumi baked a batch of cookies, yet nobody wanted to eat one.

Mini needs to finish her paper now, or she will have to finish at recess.

Lyla raced to the post office, but it was already closed.

Mom hemmed my pants, so I won't step on the bottoms.

Tina's pencil broke, so she sharpened it.

The puppy begged for a treat, but no one gave him one.

Tanya fell asleep at five o'clock, and she slept through the night.

Alok played with me at recess, and he promised to eat lunch with me.

Wahid missed the winning basket, so he will practise every night this week.

## Review Work

Write an *SS* above each simple subject. Underline each simple predicate with blue.

## Draft Book

Write five sentences that join independent clauses with commas and conjunctions.

Name ______________________________

# Two or One?

**independent clauses and conjunctions**

When two independent clauses are written together, they create a run-on sentence. To correct a run-on, decide where the first sentence ends and the second begins. The clauses can remain in one sentence if they are separated by a comma and a coordinating conjunction. There are seven coordinating conjunctions: *and*, *nor*, *but*, *for*, *yet*, *so* and *or*.

**example:** The stars were coming out the moon wasn't up yet. =
The stars were coming out, but the moon wasn't up yet.

**Separate each run-on sentence with a comma and a conjunction. Rewrite each sentence correctly on the line. Circle each comma and coordinating conjunction.**

Jaya caught a starfish she didn't keep it.

______________________________________________

The sun was bright it burned my shoulders.

______________________________________________

Zafar answered every question they were all wrong.

______________________________________________

Hema had two sandwiches she gave one to Ravi.

______________________________________________

The snow was great for packing Leela made a snowman.

______________________________________________

Our class was studying sedimentary rocks Ali brought in a fossil.

______________________________________________

## Review Work

Underline the nouns with yellow and the verbs with blue.

## Draft Book

Write five sentences that join independent clauses with commas and conjunctions.

Name ________________________________

# Breaking run-on sentences

When two independent clauses are written together, they create a run-on sentence. To avoid a run-on, decide where the first sentence ends and the second begins. A run-on can be corrected by separating it into two sentences by adding punctuation and an uppercase letter.

**example:** The lion is huge he looks fierce. = The lion is huge. He looks fierce.

**Separate the run-on sentences. Rewrite them correctly on the lines.**

Jafar has a brother his name is Rahim.

________________________________________

The clouds were dark they looked like rain clouds.

________________________________________

That bench is wet it was just painted.

________________________________________

Trisha's nose is runny she has a cold.

________________________________________

Ajay would like a dog he wants one with shaggy hair.

________________________________________

I love eating watermelon they are so juicy.

________________________________________

## Review Work

Choose two of the run-on sentences above and rewrite them. Join the independent clauses with commas and conjunctions.

## Draft Book

Look through the writing in your Draft Book for run-on sentences and correct them.

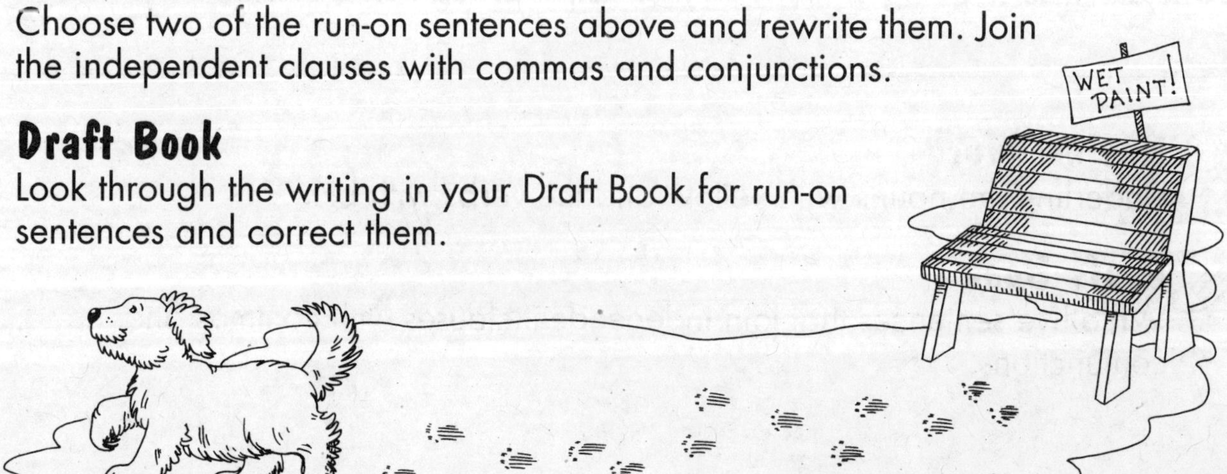

Name ______________________________

# Stop and Start

## run-on sentences

When two independent clauses are written together, they create a run-on sentence. To avoid a run-on, decide where the first sentence ends and the second begins. A run-on can be corrected by separating it into two sentences by adding punctuation and an uppercase letter.

**example:** Niraj is helpful he sets the table every night. =
Niraj is helpful. He sets the table every night.

**Separate the run-on sentences. Put a punctuation mark at the end of the first sentence. Cross out the lowercase letter and write an uppercase letter above it to begin the second sentence.**

Rohan has a new backpack it is green with many zippers.

Ray needs a paper clip he needs it to hold his papers.

Swati borrowed my pencil she plans to make a map.

It is so cold the driveway is full of ice.

Jaya is outside she is on the swings.

Aman is helping Dad Misha is helping Dad, too.

Ria read that book she recommended it to the class.

Tara found a baby squirrel it was lying at the bottom of that tree.

Zafar loves cinnamon rolls the ones with the nuts are his favourite.

Turn off the light it has been on too long.

### Review Work

Underline the complete subjects once and the complete predicates twice.

### Draft Book

Write 10 run-on sentences. Trade with a partner and correct the run-on sentences by separating them into complete sentences.

Name ________________________________

# What Do We Have Here?

**commas in a series**

Commas are used to group three or more common words.

**nouns =** Abhay, Jyoti and Zulfikar went skiing.
**verbs =** Manas can race, hurdle and jump.
**adjectives =** This muddy, red, cotton shirt should be washed in cold water.
**adverbs =** The bee flew over, under and around our desks.

**Circle each comma. Write whether it is separating nouns, verbs, adjectives or adverbs.**

Jay slowly, quietly and carefully tiptoes past the sleeping baby. ____________

Malati drew a picture of the large, bright, sunny yard. ____________

The golf ball bounced, rolled and dropped into the cup. ____________

Tanya gulped the glass of fresh, icy, sour lemonade. ____________

Varun saw emeralds, garnets and rubies in the glass case. ____________

Ria rolled, folded and taped the paper around the present. ____________

I love fresh, warm, crisp, chocolate chip cookies. ____________

Samad, Benny, Veena and Brinda watched the movie. ____________

Sign your name clearly, carefully, yet quickly. ____________

They played, swam and ate at the beach. ____________

Manu was cranky, tired and hungry. ____________

Sanjeev peeled, dipped and ate the shrimp. ____________

## Review Work

Find the sentence with predicate adjectives. Draw a star next to it.

## Draft Book

Write 10 sentences each with a list of three or more words. Put commas between the words in the lists.

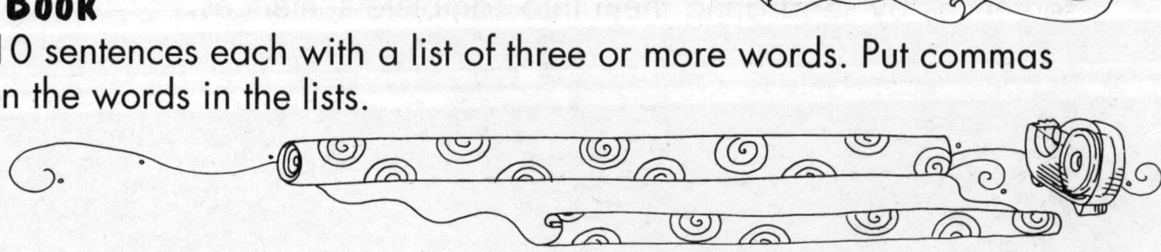

Name ______________________________

# Tell Me How Many

**commas in a series**

Commas are used to group three or more common words or word groups. Do not use a comma before *and* and *or* in a series.

**Circle each comma. Answer the question.**

Nilam, Sandra, Raghu, Bharat, Omar, Gopika, Jameela and I were in the same group on the field trip.

How many people were in the group? ______________

Smita needs to wash her face, brush her teeth, comb her hair and change her socks before we leave.

How many things does Smita need to do? ______________

We have green beans, baby carrots, potatoes, lettuce, spinach and cucumbers in the refrigerator.

How many types of vegetables are in the refrigerator? ______________

Our ice cream choices are vanilla, chocolate, strawberry, caramel nut or cheesecake.

How many flavour choices are there? ______________

**Include three other things that could be found in the woods. Add commas where needed.**

Paroma found a beetle ______________ ______________ and

______________ on her walk through the woods.

## Review Work

Underline the nouns with yellow and the verbs with blue.

## Draft Book

Chose one of the above sentences and illustrate it.

Name ______________________________

# Commas in Dates

**commas**

A comma is a type of punctuation mark used to separate a group of three or more words in a list or series. Commas are also used in certain dates to separate the day of the week, the month and date, and the year.

yes: Tuesday, July 15
yes: Tuesday, July 15, 2003
yes: July 15, 2003
no: July 15
no: July 2003

**Add commas and uppercase letters where needed in the dates.**

monday august 19 1991

november 4 2000

wednesday march 26

december 1999

sunday september 12

friday january 17

april 1

thursday july 31 2003

february 1962

october 26 1998

Trish was born sunday january 6 2002.

Soma's birthday is june 29.

Tej started kindergarten tuesday august 27 2002.

Pinky will graduate in june 2012.

The programme is thursday february 15.

## Review Work

Choose two complete dates that include the day of the week, month, date and year. Rewrite them using abbreviations.

______________________________

______________________________

## Draft Book

Write 10 sentences using dates. Add commas where needed.

Name ____________________________________

# Now Read This

## quotation marks

Some titles need quotation marks around them.

**article titles from magazines and newspapers:** I read "Drums Are Beating" in the Wednesday paper.

**chapter titles in a book:** The chapter "Moon Phases" was interesting.

**song and poem titles:** We sang "Row, Row, Row Your Boat" in music today.

Book titles, however, do not need quotation marks. Book titles are underlined.

**Add quotation marks where they belong. Underline book titles.**

The chapter Summertime in the book A Year with Me talked about gardening.

I will read No Bikes Allowed when you hand me the newspaper.

The headline on this page says Meteor Shower Tonight.

Leelaa played Marching Along on her flute.

Zafar's favourite song is Tennis Shoe Run.

Did you read Evermore Evening? I'm on the fifth chapter called Stars Come Out.

You should read this article called How to Be Nice to Your Little Sister.

Anup's birds like to sing when Birdie Bop plays on the radio.

I think the poem Bellybutton is funny.

Kali's favourite book is Up and Down.

### Review Work

Underline the simple predicates with blue.

### Draft Book

Write eight sentences using titles. Use the skill learned on this page to punctuate titles.

Name ______________________________

# My Turn

## quotation marks

Direct quotations are treated in a special way. The first word of a direct quotation is capitalised. Quotation marks go around the words people say. Punctuation at the end or at a break in the direct quote goes inside the quotation marks.

**example:** "You did a great job!" said Tinku. "This is fun," said Rinku.

**Add quotation marks around the words people say. Circle all uppercase letters and punctuation inside quotation marks.**

Knock it off, growled Anand.

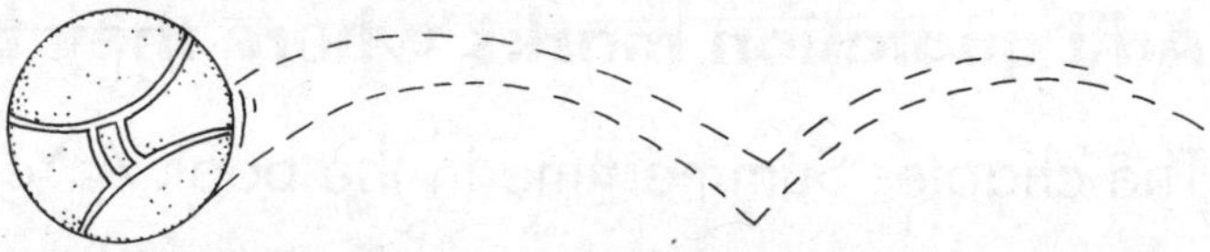

Make me! yelled Tara.

Hey, wait a minute, interrupted Jan. That's no way to solve a problem.

You're right, agreed Anand. Listen, Tara, I wanted you to stop jumping in front of me. I'm trying to make a basket.

Yeah, but I've asked you bunches of times if I could have a turn, and you've ignored me, retorted Tara.

You did? questioned Anand.

Yes, I did, answered Tara. That's the only class ball, and you told me this morning we could share it.

I did, didn't I, gulped Anand, But you still didn't have to get mad. You could have just talked to me then.

I guess, said Tara. I was just so frustrated that I yelled. I shouldn't have. Sorry.

Apology accepted, said Anand. I'm sorry I ignored you. I'll have to concentrate on listening better.

Thanks, accepted Tara. So, how about giving me a turn?

### Review Work

Underline the verbs used in place of *said* with blue.

### Draft Book

Write a story that contains direct quotations. Use the skills learned from this page to add quotation marks and punctuation.

Name ______________________________

# Dear Friend

**friendly letters**

Letters have five parts: date, greeting, body, closing and signature. The words in greetings and closings begin with uppercase letters. They end with commas. The greeting, closing and signature have their own lines.

January 2, 2002 ← date

Dear Grandpa, ← greeting

Thank you for taking me fishing. I liked catching all of those fish. They tasted great for dinner. I hope we catch more when we go again. ← body

Love, ← closing

Trishita ← signature

**Fill in the missing parts to these letters. Label each part.**

______________________________ ← ______________

Dear ____________________ , ← ______________

You are invited to my house for a sleepover. Please let me know if you can come. ← body

Sincerely, ← closing

Neha Rajan ← signature

---

______________________________ ← ______________

______________________________ ← ______________

I went to the library on Monday. I chose five books and listened to a great storyteller. I hope you can meet me there next Monday. ← body

______________________________ ← ______________

______________________________ ← ______________

## Review Work

Circle all uppercase letters and punctuation marks.

## Draft Book

Write a letter to a friend. Include all of the parts listed above.

Name ____________________

# Not Correct

**review**

**The sentences below have many mistakes. Rewrite the sentences and make the corrections.**

the box of apples are in the trunk of jairams car

yous is mean said ali you never share with me and john

ram sat lays and digging in the dirt at tunnel park

mine cup of nuts are on the counter dont eat it

i and jason went to konark orissa on monday october 14

why is they're to candy bars instead of five

i preet and joy is hear we wants too watching the movie

Name ______________________________

# Identify the Parts

**review**

**Tell as much about each sentence as you can. What kind of sentence is it? What tense is it written in? Underline nouns with yellow and verbs with blue. Draw boxes around adjectives. Circle adverbs with purple.**

Megha and Madhu will kick the ball.

kind: ☐ declarative ☐ interrogative ☐ exclamatory ☐ imperative
tense: ☐ past ☐ present ☐ future

The shoes with red laces were lost.

kind: ☐ declarative ☐ interrogative ☐ exclamatory ☐ imperative
tense: ☐ past ☐ present ☐ future

Did a little redbird quickly fly past?

kind: ☐ declarative ☐ interrogative ☐ exclamatory ☐ imperative
tense: ☐ past ☐ present ☐ future

This ice cream is delicious!

kind: ☐ declarative ☐ interrogative ☐ exclamatory ☐ imperative
tense: ☐ past ☐ present ☐ future

Name ________________________________

# Student Editing Checklist

**Check each highlighted item***

- ☐ Each sentence contains a complete subject and a complete predicate.
- ☐ Each sentence can be identified as one of the following:
  ☐ Declarative ☐ Interrogative ☐ Exclamatory ☐ Imperative
- ☐ Sentences that can be combined have been combined.
- ☐ There are no run-on sentences.
- ☐ The first letter in each sentence is capitalised, including the first letter inside quotation marks.
- ☐ The pronoun I is always capitalised.
- ☐ Each word that names a day, month or holiday starts with an uppercase letter.
- ☐ Each proper noun starts with an uppercase letter.
- ☐ Each title starts with an uppercase letter.
- ☐ Each declarative or imperative sentence ends with a full stop.
- ☐ Each interrogative sentence ends with a question mark.
- ☐ Each exclamatory sentence ends with an exclamation mark.
- ☐ Commas are used to separate dates.
- ☐ Commas are used in the greeting and closing in a letter.
- ☐ Commas are used in a list or series of three or more words.
- ☐ A comma is used between a city and state.
- ☐ Two independent clauses are joined with a conjunction and a comma.
- ☐ Abbreviations end with full stops.
- ☐ Quotation marks are used around direct quotations and certain titles.
- ☐ Book titles are underlined.

* Teacher highlights items for individual student edit.

Name ____________________________

# Student Editing Checklist

- ☐ A plural noun usually ends in *s* or *es.*
- ☐ A possessive noun usually ends in *'s.*
- ☐ Subject pronouns come before verbs.
- ☐ Object pronouns come after verbs.
- ☐ Possessive pronouns take the place of possessive nouns.
- ☐ All verb tenses correctly describe when something is happening.
- ☐ Singular verbs follow singular nouns.
- ☐ Plural verbs follow plural nouns.
- ☐ Words are spelt correctly for their meanings.
- ☐ Articles are used before nouns or adjective/noun combinations.
- ☐ Apostrophes take the place of dropped letters in contractions.

☐ Other:

____________________________

____________________________

____________________________

Answer Key

## Page 6

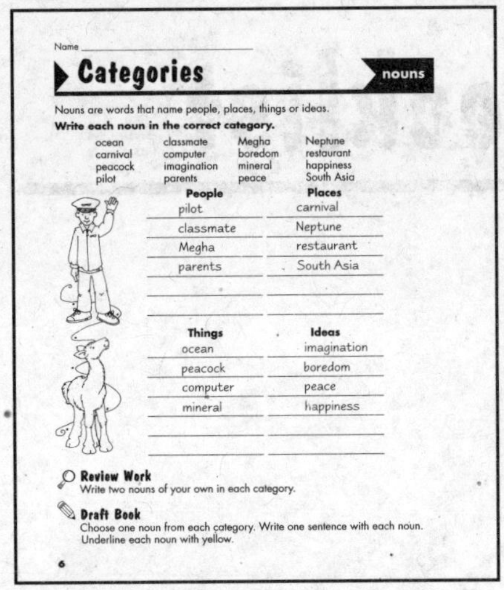
Name

**Categories** nouns

Nouns are words that name people, places, things or ideas.

**Write each noun in the correct category.**

ocean, carnival, peacock, pilot, classmate, computer, imagination, parents, Megha, boredom, mineral, peace, Neptune, restaurant, happiness, South Asia

| People | Places |
|---|---|
| pilot | carnival |
| classmate | Neptune |
| Megha | restaurant |
| parents | South Asia |

| Things | Ideas |
|---|---|
| ocean | imagination |
| peacock | boredom |
| computer | peace |
| mineral | happiness |

**Review Work** Write two nouns of your own in each category.

**Draft Book** Choose one noun from each category. Write one sentence with each noun. Underline each noun with yellow.

6

RW: Answers will vary. DB: Answers will vary.

## Page 7

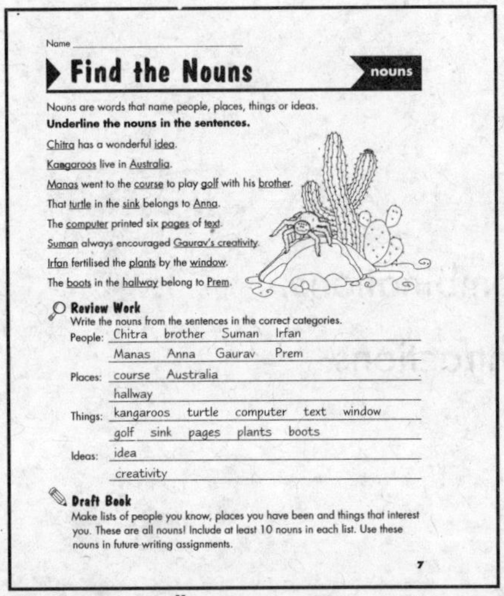
Name

**Find the Nouns** nouns

Nouns are words that name people, places, things or ideas.

**Underline the nouns in the sentences.**

Chitra has a wonderful idea.
Kangaroos live in Australia.
Manas went to the course to play golf with his brother.
That turtle in the sink belongs to Anna.
The computer printed six pages of text.
Suman always encouraged Gaurav's creativity.
Irfan fertilised the plants by the window.
The boots in the hallway belong to Prem.

**Review Work** Write the nouns from the sentences in the correct categories.

People: Chitra brother Suman Irfan Manas Anna Gaurav Prem
Places: course Australia hallway
Things: kangaroos turtle computer text window golf sink pages plants boots
Ideas: idea creativity

**Draft Book** Make lists of people you know, places you have been and things that interest you. These are all nouns! Include at least 10 nouns in each list. Use these nouns in future writing assignments.

7

DB: Answers will vary.

## Page 8

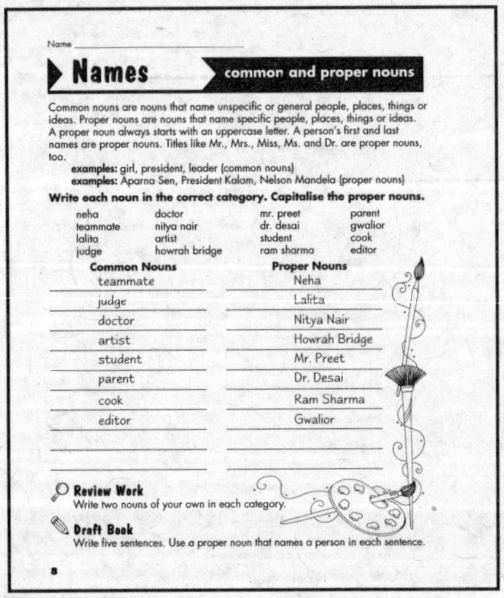
Name

**Names** common and proper nouns

Common nouns are nouns that name unspecific or general people, places, things or ideas. Proper nouns are nouns that name specific people, places, things or ideas. A proper noun always starts with an uppercase letter. A person's first and last names are proper nouns. Titles like Mr., Mrs., Miss, Ms. and Dr. are proper nouns, too.

examples: girl, president, leader (common nouns)
examples: Aparna Sen, President Kalam, Nelson Mandela (proper nouns)

**Write each noun in the correct category. Capitalise the proper nouns.**

neha, teammate, lalita, judge, doctor, nitya nair, artist, howrah bridge, mr. preet, dr. desai, student, ram sharma, parent, gwalior, cook, editor

| Common Nouns | Proper Nouns |
|---|---|
| teammate | Neha |
| judge | Lalita |
| doctor | Nitya Nair |
| artist | Howrah Bridge |
| student | Mr. Preet |
| parent | Dr. Desai |
| cook | Ram Sharma |
| editor | Gwalior |

**Review Work** Write two nouns of your own in each category.

**Draft Book** Write five sentences. Use a proper noun that names a person in each sentence.

8

RW: Answers will vary. DB: Answers will vary.

## Page 9

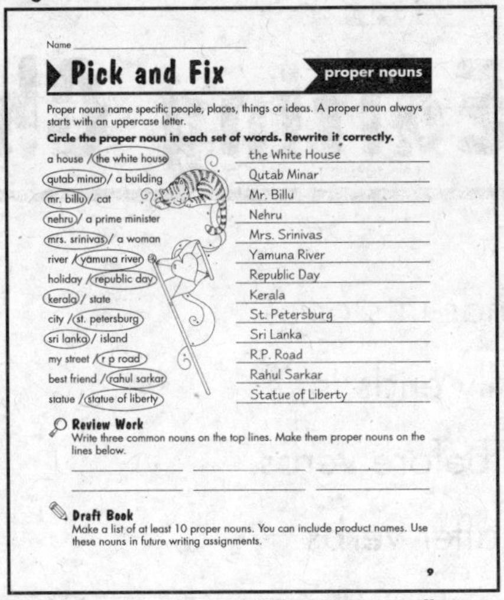
Name

**Pick and Fix** proper nouns

Proper nouns name specific people, places, things or ideas. A proper noun always starts with an uppercase letter.

**Circle the proper noun in each set of words. Rewrite it correctly.**

a house / the white house — the White House
qutab minar / a building — Qutab Minar
mr. billu / cat — Mr. Billu
nehru / a prime minister — Nehru
mrs. srinivas / a woman — Mrs. Srinivas
river / yamuna river — Yamuna River
holiday / republic day — Republic Day
kerala / state — Kerala
city / st. petersburg — St. Petersburg
sri lanka / island — Sri Lanka
my street / r p road — R.P. Road
best friend / rahul sarkar — Rahul Sarkar
statue / statue of liberty — Statue of Liberty

**Review Work** Write three common nouns on the top lines. Make them proper nouns on the lines below.

**Draft Book** Make a list of at least 10 proper nouns. You can include product names. Use these nouns in future writing assignments.

9

RW: Answers will vary. DB: Answers will vary.

## Page 10

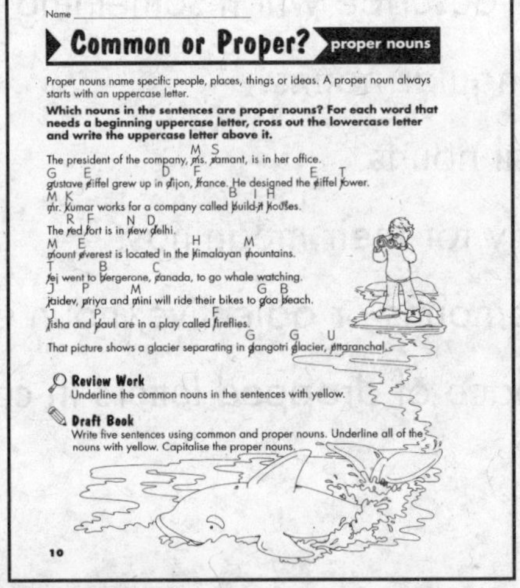
Name

**Common or Proper?** proper nouns

Proper nouns name specific people, places, things or ideas. A proper noun always starts with an uppercase letter.

**Which nouns in the sentences are proper nouns? For each word that needs a beginning uppercase letter, cross out the lowercase letter and write the uppercase letter above it.**

The president of the company, ms. sumant, is in her office. (M S)
gustave eiffel grew up in dijon, france. He designed the eiffel tower. (G E D F E T)
mr. kumar works for a company called build it houses. (M K B I H)
The red fort is in new delhi. (R F N D)
mount everest is located in the himalayan mountains. (M E H M)
jai went to bergerone, canada, to go whale watching. (J B C)
jaidev, priya and mini will ride their bikes to goa beach. (J P M G B)
jisha and paul are in a play called fireflies. (J P F)
That picture shows a glacier separating in gangotri glacier, uttaranchal. (G G U)

**Review Work** Underline the common nouns in the sentences with yellow.

**Draft Book** Write five sentences using common and proper nouns. Underline all of the nouns with yellow. Capitalise the proper nouns.

10

RW: Underline president, company, office, company, whale watching, bikes, play, picture and glacier with yellow.
DB: Answers will vary.

## Page 11

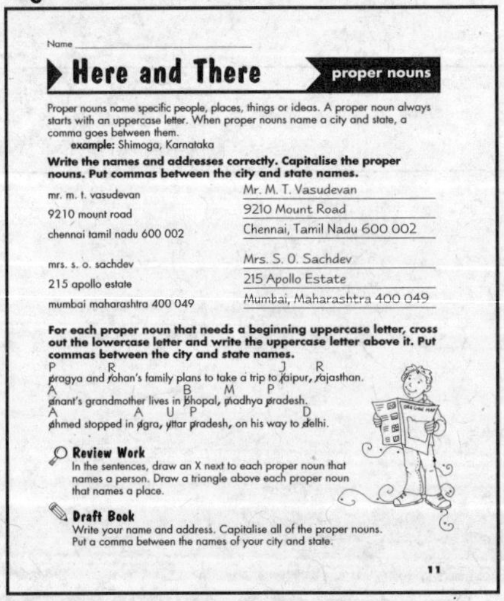
Name

**Here and There** proper nouns

Proper nouns name specific people, places, things or ideas. A proper noun always starts with an uppercase letter. When proper nouns name a city and state, a comma goes between them.

example: Shimoga, Karnataka

**Write the names and addresses correctly. Capitalise the proper nouns. Put commas between the city and state names.**

mr. m. t. vasudevan / 9210 mount road / chennai tamil nadu 600 002 — Mr. M. T. Vasudevan / 9210 Mount Road / Chennai, Tamil Nadu 600 002

mrs. s. o. sachdev / 215 apollo estate / mumbai maharashtra 400 049 — Mrs. S. O. Sachdev / 215 Apollo Estate / Mumbai, Maharashtra 400 049

**For each proper noun that needs a beginning uppercase letter, cross out the lowercase letter and write the uppercase letter above it. Put commas between the city and state names.**

pragya and rohan's family plans to take a trip to jaipur, rajasthan. (P R J R)
anant's grandmother lives in bhopal, madhya pradesh. (A B M P)
ahmed stopped in agra, uttar pradesh, on his way to delhi. (A A U P D)

**Review Work** In the sentences, draw an X next to each proper noun that names a person. Draw a triangle above each proper noun that names a place.

**Draft Book** Write your name and address. Capitalise all of the proper nouns. Put a comma between the names of your city and state.

11

RW: Draw an X next to Pragya, Rohan, Anant and Ahmed. Draw a triangle above Jaipur, Rajasthan; Bhopal, Madhya Pradesh; Agra, Uttar Pradesh; and Delhi. DB: Answers will vary.

## Page 12

Draw lines to match company/Co., boulevard/Blvd., street/St., avenue/Ave., road/Rd., United States of America/USA, and doctor/Dr. RW: Answers will vary. DB Answers will vary.

## Page 13

Draw lines to match days and months with their correct abbreviations. Rewrite sentences without abbreviations.
RW: Underline Cindy, Vine St., lessons, Monday, Wednesday, Friday, months, Jammu, December, January and February with yellow.
DB: Answers will vary.

## Page 14

Name

**Make It Singular** singular and plural nouns

A noun can be singular (one person, place, thing or idea) or plural (more than one). Usually, a noun becomes plural by adding an s to the end. Sometimes, a noun becomes singular by removing the s from the end.

**Make the plural nouns singular. Use the nouns to finish the sentences. Decide if the plural or singular noun works best in each sentence.**

turtles — turtle
Kavita found one painted turtle.
Vinu found five box turtles.
bears — bear
Shan saw three baby bears.
Vinay saw an angry bear.
ferrets — ferret
Pooja owns a brown ferret.
The pet store has many ferrets.
lizards — lizard
Ayan caught that lizard in a tree.
He tried to catch other lizards, but they ran away.

**Which words helped you decide whether you needed a singular or plural noun in each sentence? Circle the words that helped you. The first one has been done for you.**

**Review Work** Underline the other nouns in the sentences with yellow.

**Draft Book** Write a paragraph about your favourite animal. Underline all of the nouns in the paragraph with yellow. Circle any plural nouns.

14

RW: Underline Kavita, Vinu, Shan, Vinay, Pooja, store and Ayan with yellow.
DB: Answers will vary.

## Page 15

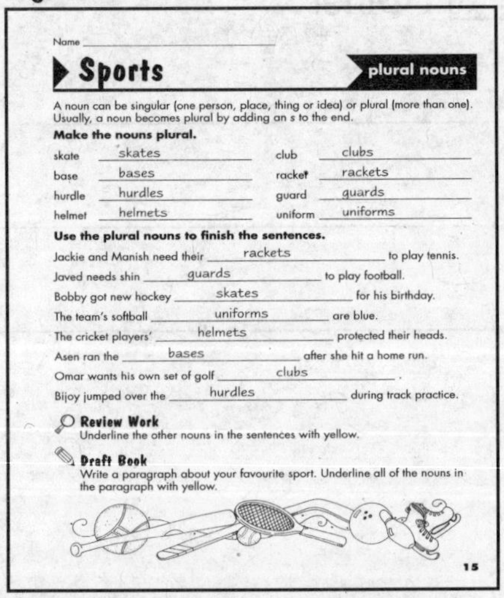
Name

**Sports** plural nouns

A noun can be singular (one person, place, thing or idea) or plural (more than one). Usually, a noun becomes plural by adding an s to the end.

**Make the nouns plural.**

| | | | |
|---|---|---|---|
| skate | skates | club | clubs |
| base | bases | racket | rackets |
| hurdle | hurdles | guard | guards |
| helmet | helmets | uniform | uniforms |

**Use the plural nouns to finish the sentences.**

Jackie and Manish need their rackets to play tennis.
Javed needs shin guards to play football.
Bobby got new hockey skates for his birthday.
The team's softball uniforms are blue.
The cricket players' helmets protected their heads.
Asen ran the bases after she hit a home run.
Omar wants his own set of golf clubs.
Bijoy jumped over the hurdles during track practice.

**Review Work** Underline the other nouns in the sentences with yellow.

**Draft Book** Write a paragraph about your favourite sport. Underline all of the nouns in the paragraph with yellow.

15

RW: Underline Jackie, Manish, tennis, Javed, football, Bobby, birthday, team's, players', heads, Asen, home run, Omar, Bijoy and practice with yellow.
DB: Answers will vary.

**Answer Key**

## Page 16

Name ______

### Creatures — plural nouns

A noun can be singular (one person, place, thing or idea) or plural (more than one). Sometimes, a noun becomes plural by adding es to the end.
**example:** crutch → crut**ches** **example:** class → classes
**example:** dish → di**shes** **example:** box → boxes

**Make the nouns plural.**

| | | | |
|---|---|---|---|
| lunch | lunches | dash | dashes |
| pouch | pouches | crunch | crunches |
| dress | dresses | brush | brushes |
| finch | finches | tax | taxes |
| fox | foxes | branch | branches |

**Use some of the plural nouns to finish the sentences.**

My dad packed lunches for my brother and me.

There are three brushes on the bathroom counter.

Kangaroos, opossums and koalas use their pouches to carry their young.

The branches of the tree were filled with finches building nests.

**Review Work**
Underline the other nouns in the sentences with yellow.

**Draft Book**
Make a list of nouns that become plural by adding es to the end of each. Start with the words on this page. Write the singular and plural forms of the words. Use these nouns in future writings.

16

**RW: Underline dad, brother, counter, kangaroos, opossums, koalas, young, tree and nests with yellow. DB: Answers will vary.**

## Page 17

Name ______

### Different Endings — plural nouns

A noun can be singular (one person, place, thing or idea) or plural (more than one). Usually, a noun becomes plural by adding an s to the end. A noun that ends with ch, s, z, sh or x becomes plural by adding es to the end. A noun that ends with f or fe becomes plural by changing the f or fe to v and adding es to the end.
**example:** calf → cal**ves** **example:** scarf → scar**ves**

**Make the nouns plural.**

| | | | |
|---|---|---|---|
| leaf | leaves | coach | coaches |
| half | halves | knife | knives |
| bench | benches | bunch | bunches |
| glass | glasses | lunch | lunches |

**Write the other form of each noun.**

Red, yellow and orange leaves (leaf) are falling from the trees.

Please put the dishes (dish), glasses (glass), knives (knife) and forks (fork) on the table.

For lunch (lunches), Chitra had two halves (half) of a sandwich and a bunch (bunches) of grapes (grape).

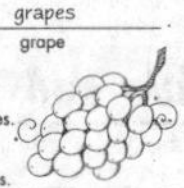

**Review Work**
Draw a star above each singular noun in the sentences.

**Draft Book**
Two of the plural nouns were not used in the sentences. Write a sentence with each word. Underline the nouns with yellow.

17

**RW: Draw a star above table, lunch, Chitra, sandwich and bunch. DB: Answers will vary.**

## Page 18

Name ______

### Here Come the Ys — plural nouns

A noun can be singular (one person, place, thing or idea) or plural (more than one). There are two rules for making a noun that ends with y plural. For a noun that ends with a consonant + y, change the y to i and add es to the end. For a noun that ends with a vowel + y, add an s to the end.
**example:** lady → ladies **example:** toy → toys

**Make the nouns plural.**

Tanya has seventeen guppies (guppy) in her aquarium.

Did you forget your house keys (key) again?

Sometimes raccoons climb into chimneys (chimney) to make nests.

How many rupees (rupee) do you have in your bank?

Wild turkeys (turkey) live in the woods by Jan's house.

Mridul loves to have strawberries (strawberry) on his ice cream.

Gopan has read many stories (story) about monkeys (monkey) living in the rain forests.

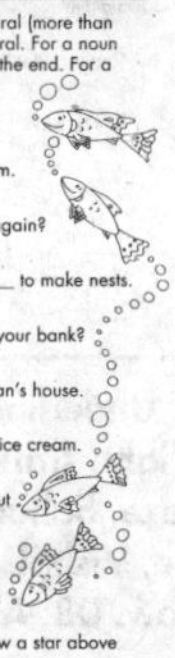

**Review Work**
Underline the other nouns in the sentences with yellow. Draw a star above each singular noun.

**Draft Book**
Make these nouns plural: baby, pony, boy and cherry. Use the plural nouns to write four sentences. Circle the plural nouns. Draw a star above each singular noun.

18

**RW: Underline Tanya, aquarium, raccoons, nests, bank, woods, house, Mridul, ice cream, Gopan and rain forests with yellow. Draw a star above Tanya, aquarium, bank, house, Mridul, ice cream and Gopan. DB: Answers will vary.**

## Page 19

Name ______

### Make Mine Plural — plural nouns

A noun can be singular (one person, place, thing or idea) or plural (more than one).

**Make the nouns plural.**

| | | | |
|---|---|---|---|
| mess | messes | hobby | hobbies |
| wish | wishes | thief | thieves |
| wife | wives | donkey | donkeys |
| peach | peaches | daisy | daisies |
| dog | dogs | mass | masses |
| way | ways | rash | rashes |
| berry | berries | ray | rays |
| life | lives | baby | babies |
| crash | crashes | sky | skies |
| toy | toys | watch | watches |
| shelf | shelves | bay | bays |
| class | classes | candy | candies |
| elf | elves | day | days |

**Review Work**
Write each singular noun from above that ends with y but does not have es when it becomes plural.
way, toy, donkey, ray, bay, day

**Draft Book**
Choose five pairs of nouns (a pair includes both singular and plural forms). Write a sentence with each noun.

19

**DB: Answers will vary.**

## Page 20

**Draw lines to match ox/oxen, tooth/teeth, child/children, foot/feet, person/people, octopus/octopuses or octopi, man/men, woman/women and bus/buses. Circle children, buses, octopuses, people, teeth, deer, sheep, men, series, women and feet. RW: Underline aquarium, creatures, animals, zoo, tickets, playoffs and race. DB: Answers will vary.**

## Page 21

Name ______

### Mine, All Mine — possessive nouns

A possessive noun shows belonging. If a noun is singular or if it is plural but does not end with an s, add an apostrophe + s ('s) to the end to make it possessive.
**examples:** cat's food, boss's pen, men's shoes
If a noun is plural and already ends with an s, add an apostrophe to the end.
**examples:** cats' collars, players' helmets

**Finish each sentence with a possessive noun.**

The pond belongs to those frogs. It is the frogs' pond.

The crayons belong Divya. They are Divya's crayons.

The bats belong to those boys. They are the boys' bats.

The swing belongs to Manas. It is Manas's swing.

The hill belongs to the ants. It is the ants' hill.

The hat belongs to Mohit. It is Mohit's hat.

Those marbles belong to Louis. They are Louis's marbles.

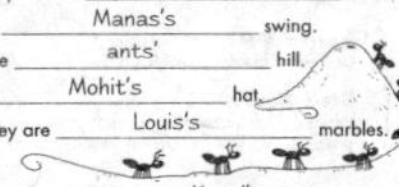

**Make the nouns possessive.**

| | | | |
|---|---|---|---|
| girls | girls' | Kunal | Kunal's |
| frog | frog's | Yasar | Yasar's |
| dogs | dogs' | classmates | classmate's |
| women | women's | Mr. Ram | Mr. Ram's |
| Tara | Tara's | birds | birds' |
| teachers | teachers' | turtle | turtle's |

**Review Work**
Draw a star above each singular noun in the sentences. Circle the plural nouns.

**Draft Book**
Write ten sentences with possessive nouns. Use both singular and plural nouns. Underline the nouns with yellow.

21

**RW: Draw a star above pond, pond, Divya, swing, Manas, swing, hill, hill, hat, Mohit, hat and Louis. Circle frogs, crayons, crayons, bats, boys, bats, ants, marbles, marbles. DB: Answers will vary.**

## Page 22

Name ______

### Who Owns It? — possessive nouns

A possessive noun shows belonging. If a noun is singular or if it is plural but does not end with an s, add an apostrophe + s ('s) to the end to make it possessive.
**examples:** cat's food, boss's pen, men's shoes
If a noun is plural and already ends with an s, add an apostrophe to the end.
**examples:** cats' collars, players' helmets

**Circle the possessive noun in each sentence. How many people or things possess something? Circle 1 if one person or thing possesses something. Circle 2+ if more than one person or thing possesses something.**

| | | |
|---|---|---|
| (1) | 2+ | The audience laughed at the (comedian's) performance. |
| 1 | (2+) | The (turtles') pond needs a log in it. |
| (1) | 2+ | The (dancer's) shoes had holes in them. |
| (1) | 2+ | A (book's) pages must be treated gently. |
| 1 | (2+) | The (chipmunks') home is stuffed with bird seed. |
| 1 | (2+) | Can you sharpen the (students') pencils? |
| (1) | 2+ | The (museum's) admission price is Rs. 3.00. |
| (1) | 2+ | Lisa let (Chirag's) five birds out of their cages. |
| (1) | 2+ | The (bluebird's) nest has three eggs. |
| (1) | 2+ | Hakim borrowed the (team's) score book. |
| 1 | (2+) | Sandra washed her (parents') cars. |
| (1) | 2+ | (Omar's) cat scratched me. |

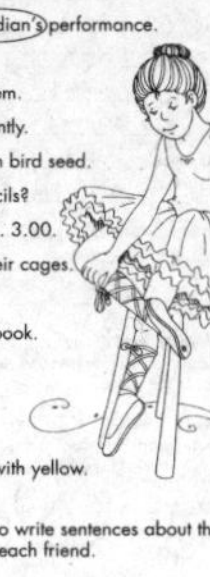

**Review Work**
Underline the other nouns in the sentences with yellow.

**Draft Book**
Choose four friends. Use possessive nouns to write sentences about things that belong to them. Write two sentences about each friend.

22

**RW: Underline audience, performance, pond, log, shoes, holes, pages, home, seed, pencils, price, Lisa, birds, cages, nest, eggs, Hakim, book, Sandra, cars and cat with yellow. DB: Answers will vary.**

## Page 23

Name ______

### Hide-and-Seek — action verbs

An action verb tells what someone or something is doing.
**example:** The boy **swings** the golf club.
**example:** The mouse **scampers** across the floor.

**Circle each action verb.**

Varun (hides) from his friend.
Manisha (searches) for the others.
Jaya (crouches) behind the slide.
Ram (crawls) along the fence.
Salma (jumps) over the log.
Insects (scatter) out of the way.
Maria (giggles) behind the oak tree.
Joy (climbs) up the old maple.
The leaves on the old maple (sway) in the breeze.
Manisha (finds) Karan.
Karan (races) to the free spot.
Manisha (tags) Karan.
Karan (yells) for everyone to come out.

**Review Work**
Underline the nouns in the sentences with yellow.

**Draft Book**
Find a page in your Draft Book with the nouns underlined with yellow. Underline the verbs with blue.

23

**RW: Underline Varun, friend, Manisha, Jaya, slide, Ram, fence, Salma, log, insects, way, Maria, tree, Joy, maple, breeze, Manisha, Karan, Karan, spot, Manisha, Karan and Karan with yellow. DB: Answers will vary.**

Answer Key

## Page 24

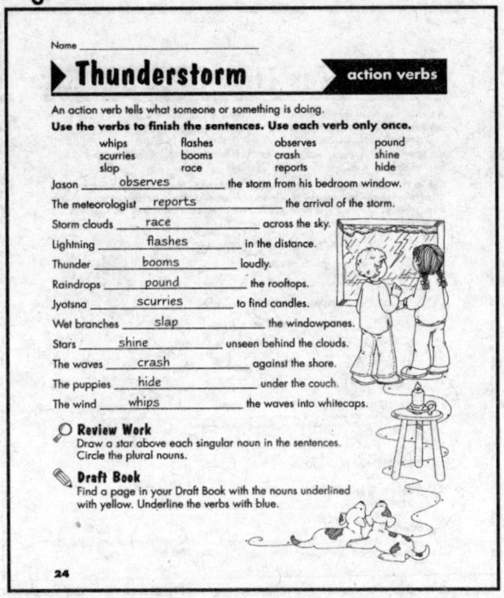
Name ____

**Thunderstorm** — action verbs

An action verb tells what someone or something is doing.

**Use the verbs to finish the sentences. Use each verb only once.**

whips, flashes, observes, pound, scurries, booms, crash, shine, slap, race, reports, hide

Jason observes the storm from his bedroom window.
The meteorologist reports the arrival of the storm.
Storm clouds race across the sky.
Lightning flashes in the distance.
Thunder booms loudly.
Raindrops pound the rooftops.
Jyotsna scurries to find candles.
Wet branches slap the windowpanes.
Stars shine unseen behind the clouds.
The waves crash against the shore.
The puppies hide under the couch.
The wind whips the waves into whitecaps.

**Review Work** Draw a star above each singular noun in the sentences. Circle the plural nouns.

**Draft Book** Find a page in your Draft Book with the nouns underlined with yellow. Underline the verbs with blue.

24

RW: Draw a star above Jason, storm, window, meteorologist, arrival, storm, sky, lightning, distance, thunder, Jyotsna, shore, couch and wind. Circle clouds, raindrops, rooftops, candles, branches, windowpanes, stars, clouds, waves, puppies, waves and whitecaps.
DB: Answers will vary.

## Page 25

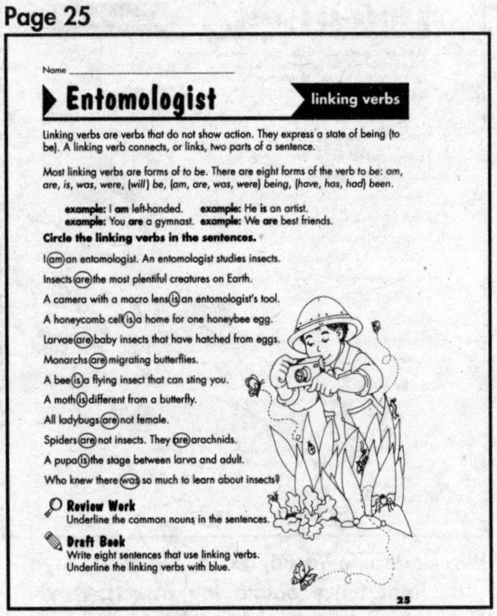
Name ____

**Entomologist** — linking verbs

Linking verbs are verbs that do not show action. They express a state of being (to be). A linking verb connects, or links, two parts of a sentence.

Most linking verbs are forms of to be. There are eight forms of the verb to be: am, are, is, was, were, (will) be, (am, are, was, were) being, (have, has, had) been.

example: I am left-handed. example: He is an artist.
example: You are a gymnast. example: We are best friends.

**Circle the linking verbs in the sentences.**

I am an entomologist. An entomologist studies insects.
Insects are the most plentiful creatures on Earth.
A camera with a macro lens is an entomologist's tool.
A honeycomb cell is a home for one honeybee egg.
Larvae are baby insects that have hatched from eggs.
Monarchs are migrating butterflies.
A bee is a flying insect that can sting you.
A moth is different from a butterfly.
All ladybugs are not female.
Spiders are not insects. They are arachnids.
A pupa is the stage between larva and adult.
Who knew there was so much to learn about insects?

**Review Work** Underline the common nouns in the sentences.

**Draft Book** Write eight sentences that use linking verbs. Underline the linking verbs with blue.

25

RW: Underline entomologist, entomologist, insects, insects, creatures, camera, lens, tool, cell, home, egg, larvae, insects, eggs, monarchs, butterflies, bee, insect, moth, butterfly, ladybugs, female, spiders, insects, arachnids, pupa, stage, larva, adult and insects. DB: Answers will vary.

## Page 26

Name ____

**Link Them Together** — linking verbs

Linking verbs are verbs that do not show action. They express a state of being. A linking verb connects, or links, two parts of a sentence. In a sentence, a linking verb comes before a noun or adjective—not an action verb.

Most linking verbs are forms of to be. There are eight forms of the verb to be: am, are, is, was, were, (will) be, (am, are, was, were) being, (have, has, had) been.

**Circle the linking verbs in the sentences.**

Rena was in the gym.
The garbage cans were full.
Hannah will be in second grade next year.
We have been patient.
Shan and James had been sick with the flu.
Those grey birds in that tree are being very noisy.
The picture above the door is one that I painted.
Matches are dangerous.
I am being careful near the baby.
Ria's hair is very short.
Richard has been asleep all afternoon.
The dinosaur fossils were very interesting.

**Review Work** Underline the common nouns in the sentences. Draw an X next to each proper noun that names a person. Draw a tick next to the possessive noun.

**Draft Book** Write eight sentences that use linking verbs. Use a variety of the verbs from this page. Underline the linking verbs with blue.

26

RW: Underline gym, cans, grade, year, flu, birds, tree, picture, door, matches, baby, hair, afternoon and fossils. Draw an X next to Rena, Hannah, Shan, James, Ria and Richard. Draw a check next to Ria's. DB: Answers will vary.

## Page 27

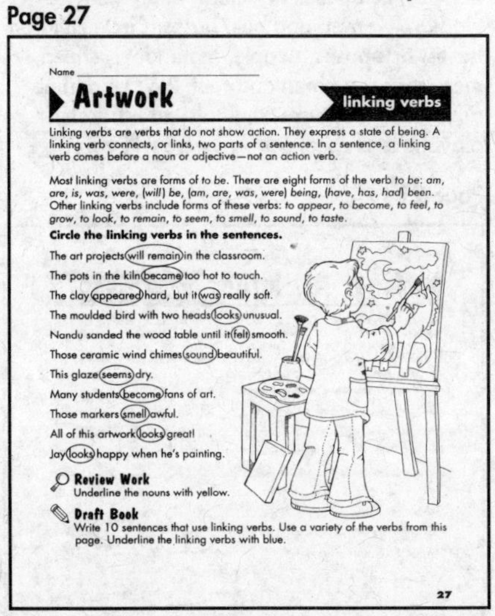
Name ____

**Artwork** — linking verbs

Linking verbs are verbs that do not show action. They express a state of being. A linking verb connects, or links, two parts of a sentence. In a sentence, a linking verb comes before a noun or adjective—not an action verb.

Most linking verbs are forms of to be. There are eight forms of the verb to be: am, are, is, was, were, (will) be, (am, are, was, were) being, (have, has, had) been. Other linking verbs include forms of these verbs: to appear, to become, to feel, to grow, to look, to remain, to seem, to smell, to sound, to taste.

**Circle the linking verbs in the sentences.**

The art projects will remain in the classroom.
The pots in the kiln became too hot to touch.
The clay appeared hard, but it was really soft.
The moulded bird with two heads looks unusual.
Nandu sanded the wood table until it felt smooth.
Those ceramic wind chimes sound beautiful.
This glaze seems dry.
Many students become fans of art.
Those markers smell awful.
All of this artwork looks great!
Jay looks happy when he's painting.

**Review Work** Underline the nouns with yellow.

**Draft Book** Write 10 sentences that use linking verbs. Use a variety of the verbs from this page. Underline the linking verbs with blue.

27

RW: Underline projects, classroom, pots, kiln, clay, bird, heads, Nandu, table, chimes, glaze, students, fans, art, markers, artwork and Jay with yellow. DB: Answers will vary.

## Page 28

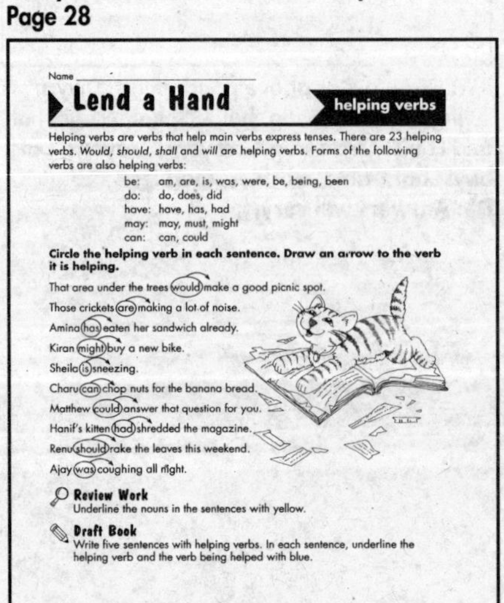
Name ____

**Lend a Hand** — helping verbs

Helping verbs are verbs that help main verbs express tenses. There are 23 helping verbs. Would, should, shall and will are helping verbs. Forms of the following verbs are also helping verbs:

be: am, are, is, was, were, be, being, been
do: do, does, did
have: have, has, had
may: may, must, might
can: can, could

**Circle the helping verb in each sentence. Draw an arrow to the verb it is helping.**

That area under the trees would make a good picnic spot.
Those crickets are making a lot of noise.
Amina has eaten her sandwich already.
Kiran might buy a new bike.
Sheila is sneezing.
Charu can chop nuts for the banana bread.
Matthew could answer that question for you.
Hanif's kitten had shredded the magazine.
Renu should rake the leaves this weekend.
Ajay was coughing all night.

**Review Work** Underline the nouns in the sentences with yellow.

**Draft Book** Write five sentences with helping verbs. In each sentence, underline the helping verb and the verb being helped with blue.

28

## Page 28 (cont.)

RW: Underline area, trees, spot, crickets, noise, Amina, sandwich, Kiran, bike, Shiela, Charu, nuts, bread, Matthew, question, Hanif's, kitten, magazine, Renu, leaves, weekend, Ajay, and night with yellow.
DB: Answers will vary.

## Page 29

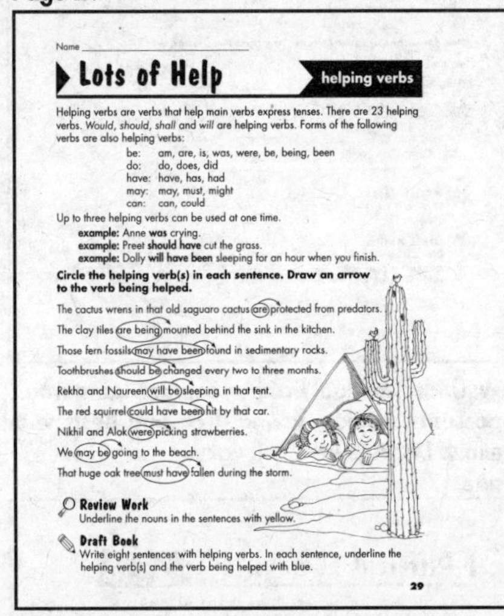
Name ____

**Lots of Help** — helping verbs

Helping verbs are verbs that help main verbs express tenses. There are 23 helping verbs. Would, should, shall and will are helping verbs. Forms of the following verbs are also helping verbs:

be: am, are, is, was, were, be, being, been
do: do, does, did
have: have, has, had
may: may, must, might
can: can, could

Up to three helping verbs can be used at one time.
example: Anne **was** crying.
example: Preet **should have** cut the grass.
example: Dolly **will have been** sleeping for an hour when you finish.

**Circle the helping verb(s) in each sentence. Draw an arrow to the verb being helped.**

The cactus wrens in that old saguaro cactus are protected from predators.
The clay tiles are being mounted behind the sink in the kitchen.
Those fern fossils may have been found in sedimentary rocks.
Toothbrushes should be changed every two to three months.
Rekha and Naureen will be sleeping in that tent.
The red squirrel could have been hit by that car.
Nikhil and Alok were picking strawberries.
We may be going to the beach.
That huge oak tree must have fallen during the storm.

**Review Work** Underline the nouns in the sentences with yellow.

**Draft Book** Write eight sentences with helping verbs. In each sentence, underline the helping verb(s) and the verb being helped with blue.

29

RW: Underline wrens, cactus, predators, tiles, sink, kitchen, fossils, rocks, toothbrushes, months, Rekha, Naureen, tent, squirrel, car, Nikhil, Alok, strawberries, beach, tree and storm with yellow. DB: Answers will vary.

Page 30: Answers will vary.

## Page 31

Name ____

**Now and Then** — past and present tense

Verbs use tenses to tell when something is happening. When the action happens now, it is present tense. When the action happened in the past, it is past tense. One way to make a verb past tense is to add ed to the end.
example: Suman **studies** for the test. (present tense)
example: Suman **studied** for the test. (past tense)

**Circle the verb in each sentence. Write whether the verb is past tense or present tense.**

The sea horse floats by the starfish. — present
The paper's colour faded in the sunlight. — past
The string tangled into a huge knot. — past
Nilesh disturbed the sleeping puppy. — past
The kites dance in the breeze. — present
Sohan sharpens his pencil. — present
Asha bandaged her finger. — past
Children tumble down the sand dune. — present
Vishal flicked the paper football. — past
Gautam defends his snow fort. — present

**Review Work** Underline the nouns in the sentences with yellow.

**Draft Book** Choose five of the sentences. If the verb is present tense, rewrite it in the past tense. If the verb is past tense, rewrite it in the present tense.

31

RW: Underline sea horse, starfish, colour, sunlight, string, knot, Nilesh, puppy, kites, breeze, Sohan, pencil, Asha, finger, children, dune, Vishal, football, Gautam and fort with yellow. DB: Answers will vary.

**Answer Key**

**Page 32**

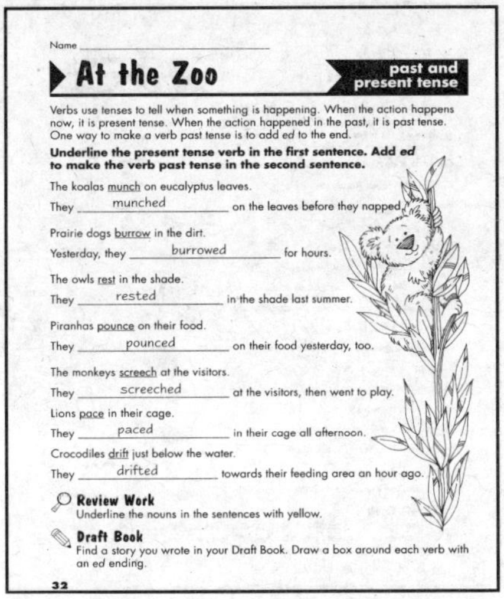

Name

# At the Zoo
past and present tense

Verbs use tenses to tell when something is happening. When the action happens now, it is present tense. When the action happened in the past, it is past tense. One way to make a verb past tense is to add *ed* to the end.

**Underline the present tense verb in the first sentence. Add *ed* to make the verb past tense in the second sentence.**

The koalas munch on eucalyptus leaves.
They munched on the leaves before they napped.
Prairie dogs burrow in the dirt.
Yesterday, they burrowed for hours.
The owls rest in the shade.
They rested in the shade last summer.
Piranhas pounce on their food.
They pounced on their food yesterday, too.
The monkeys screech at the visitors.
They screeched at the visitors, then went to play.
Lions pace in their cage.
They paced in their cage all afternoon.
Crocodiles drift just below the water.
They drifted towards their feeding area an hour ago.

**Review Work** Underline the nouns in the sentences with yellow.

**Draft Book** Find a story you wrote in your Draft Book. Draw a box around each verb with an *ed* ending.

32

**RW: Underline koalas, leaves, leaves, prairie dogs, dirt, hours, owls, shade, shade, summer, piranhas, food, food, monkeys, visitors, visitors, lions, cage, cage, afternoon, crocodiles, water, area and hour with yellow. DB: Answers will vary.**

**Page 33**

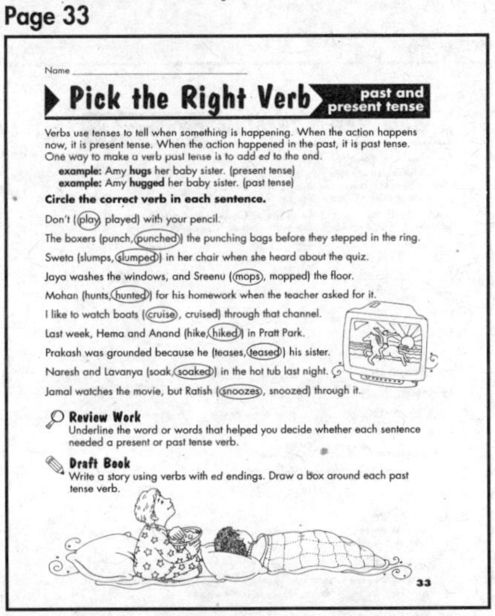

Name

# Pick the Right Verb
past and present tense

Verbs use tenses to tell when something is happening. When the action happens now, it is present tense. When the action happened in the past, it is past tense. One way to make a verb past tense is to add *ed* to the end.
**example:** Amy **hugs** her baby sister. (present tense)
**example:** Amy **hugged** her baby sister. (past tense)

**Circle the correct verb in each sentence.**

Don't (play, played) with your pencil.
The boxers (punch, punched) the punching bags before they stepped in the ring.
Sweta (slumps, slumped) in her chair when she heard about the quiz.
Jaya washes the windows, and Sreenu (mops, mopped) the floor.
Mohan (hunts, hunted) for his homework when the teacher asked for it.
I like to watch boats (cruise, cruised) through that channel.
Last week, Hema and Anand (hike, hiked) in Pratt Park.
Prakash was grounded because he (teases, teased) his sister.
Naresh and Lavanya (soak, soaked) in the hot tub last night.
Jamal watches the movie, but Ratish (snoozes, snoozed) through it.

**Review Work** Underline the word or words that helped you decide whether each sentence needed a present or past tense verb.

**Draft Book** Write a story using verbs with *ed* endings. Draw a box around each past tense verb.

33

**RW: Underline don't, stepped, heard, washes, asked, watch, last week, was grounded, last night and watches. DB: Answers will vary.**

**Page 34**

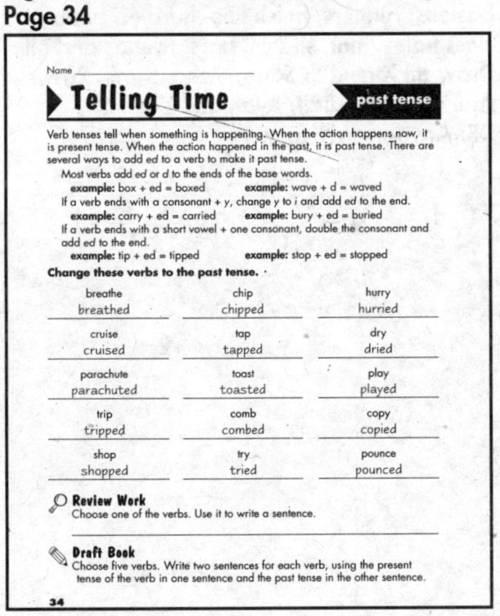

Name

# Telling Time
past tense

Verb tenses tell when something is happening. When the action happens now, it is present tense. When the action happened in the past, it is past tense. There are several ways to add *ed* to a verb to make it past tense.
Most verbs add *ed* or *d* to the ends of the base words.
**example:** box + ed = boxed **example:** wave + d = waved
If a verb ends with a consonant + *y*, change *y* to *i* and add *ed* to the end.
**example:** carry + ed = carried **example:** bury + ed = buried
If a verb ends with a short vowel + one consonant, double the consonant and add *ed* to the end.
**example:** tip + ed = tipped **example:** stop + ed = stopped

**Change these verbs to the past tense.**

| breathe | chip | hurry |
|---|---|---|
| breathed | chipped | hurried |
| cruise | tap | dry |
| cruised | tapped | dried |
| parachute | toast | play |
| parachuted | toasted | played |
| trip | comb | copy |
| tripped | combed | copied |
| shop | try | pounce |
| shopped | tried | pounced |

**Review Work** Choose one of the verbs. Use it to write a sentence.

**Draft Book** Choose five verbs. Write two sentences for each verb, using the present tense of the verb in one sentence and the past tense in the other sentence.

34

**Page 34 (cont.)**
**RW: Answers will vary. DB: Answers will vary.**

**Page 35**

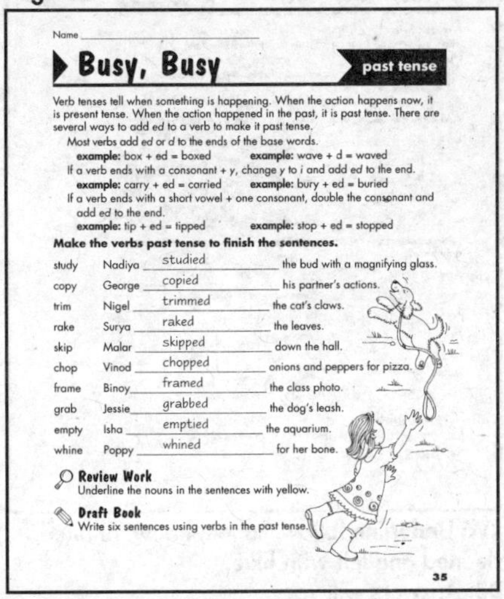

Name

# Busy, Busy
past tense

Verb tenses tell when something is happening. When the action happens now, it is present tense. When the action happened in the past, it is past tense. There are several ways to add *ed* to a verb to make it past tense.
Most verbs add *ed* or *d* to the ends of the base words.
**example:** box + ed = boxed **example:** wave + d = waved
If a verb ends with a consonant + *y*, change *y* to *i* and add *ed* to the end.
**example:** carry + ed = carried **example:** bury + ed = buried
If a verb ends with a short vowel + one consonant, double the consonant and add *ed* to the end.
**example:** tip + ed = tipped **example:** stop + ed = stopped

**Make the verbs past tense to finish the sentences.**

study Nadiya studied the bud with a magnifying glass.
copy George copied his partner's actions.
trim Nigel trimmed the cat's claws.
rake Surya raked the leaves.
skip Malar skipped down the hall.
chop Vinod chopped onions and peppers for pizza.
frame Binoy framed the class photo.
grab Jessie grabbed the dog's leash.
empty Isha emptied the aquarium.
whine Poppy whined for her bone.

**Review Work** Underline the nouns in the sentences with yellow.

**Draft Book** Write six sentences using verbs in the past tense.

35

**RW: Underline Nadiya, bud, magnifying glass, George, partner's, actions, Nigel, cat's, claws, Surya, leaves, Malar, hall, Vinod, onions, peppers, pizza, Binoy, photo, Jessie, dog's, leash, Isha, aquarium, Poppy and bone with yellow.**
**DB: Answers will vary.**

**Page 36**

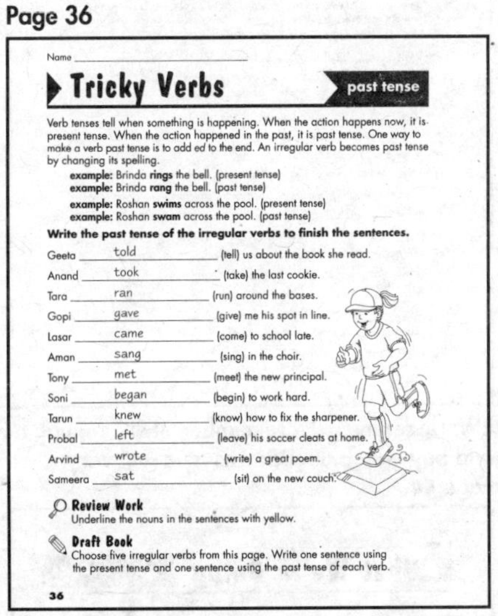

Name

# Tricky Verbs
past tense

Verb tenses tell when something is happening. When the action happens now, it is present tense. When the action happened in the past, it is past tense. One way to make a verb past tense is to add *ed* to the end. An irregular verb becomes past tense by changing its spelling.
**example:** Brinda **rings** the bell. (present tense)
**example:** Brinda **rang** the bell. (past tense)
**example:** Roshan **swims** across the pool. (present tense)
**example:** Roshan **swam** across the pool. (past tense)

**Write the past tense of the irregular verbs to finish the sentences.**

Geeta told (tell) us about the book she read.
Anand took (take) the last cookie.
Tara ran (run) around the bases.
Gopi gave (give) me his spot in line.
Lasar came (come) to school late.
Aman sang (sing) in the choir.
Tony met (meet) the new principal.
Soni began (begin) to work hard.
Tarun knew (know) how to fix the sharpener.
Probal left (leave) his soccer cleats at home.
Arvind wrote (write) a great poem.
Sameera sat (sit) on the new couch.

**Review Work** Underline the nouns in the sentences with yellow.

**Draft Book** Choose five irregular verbs from this page. Write one sentence using the present tense and one sentence using the past tense of each verb.

36

**RW: Underline Geeta, book, Anand, cookie, Tara, bases, Gopi, spot, line, Lasar, school, Aman, choir, Tony, principal, Soni, Tarun, sharpener, Probal, cleats, home, Arvind, poem, Sameera and couch with yellow.**
**DB: Answers will vary.**

**Page 37**

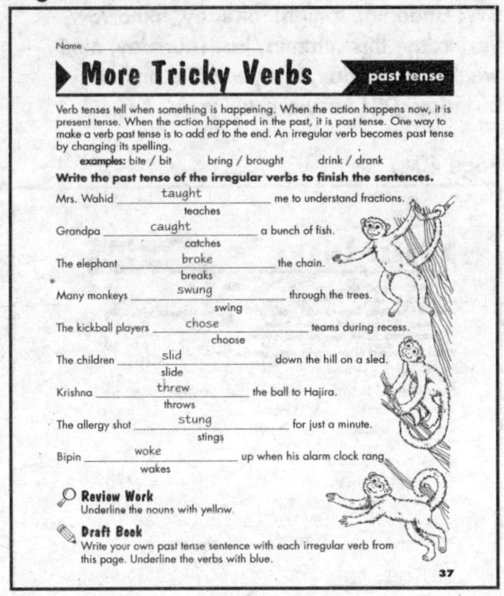

Name

# More Tricky Verbs
past tense

Verb tenses tell when something is happening. When the action happens now, it is present tense. When the action happened in the past, it is past tense. One way to make a verb past tense is to add *ed* to the end. An irregular verb becomes past tense by changing its spelling.
**examples:** bite / bit bring / brought drink / drank

**Write the past tense of the irregular verbs to finish the sentences.**

Mrs. Wahid taught (teaches) me to understand fractions.
Grandpa caught (catches) a bunch of fish.
The elephant broke (breaks) the chain.
Many monkeys swung (swing) through the trees.
The kickball players chose (choose) teams during recess.
The children slid (slide) down the hill on a sled.
Krishna threw (throws) the ball to Hajira.
The allergy shot stung (stings) for just a minute.
Bipin woke (wakes) up when his alarm clock rang.

**Review Work** Underline the nouns with yellow.

**Draft Book** Write your own past tense sentence with each irregular verb from this page. Underline the verbs with blue.

37

**RW: Underline Mrs. Wahid, fractions, Grandpa, fish, elephant, chain, monkeys, trees, players, teams, recess, children, hill, sled, Krishna, ball, Hajira, shot, minute, Bipin and alarm clock with yellow. DB: Answers will vary.**

**Page 38**

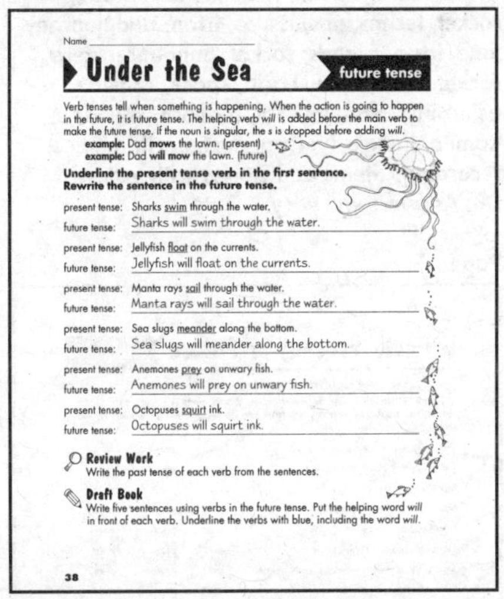

Name

# Under the Sea
future tense

Verb tenses tell when something is happening. When the action is going to happen in the future, it is future tense. The helping verb *will* is added before the main verb to make the future tense. If the noun is singular, the *s* is dropped before adding will.
**example:** Dad **mows** the lawn. (present)
**example:** Dad **will mow** the lawn. (future)

**Underline the present tense verb in the first sentence. Rewrite the sentence in the future tense.**

present tense: Sharks swim through the water.
future tense: Sharks will swim through the water.
present tense: Jellyfish float on the currents.
future tense: Jellyfish will float on the currents.
present tense: Manta rays sail through the water.
future tense: Manta rays will sail through the water.
present tense: Sea slugs meander along the bottom.
future tense: Sea slugs will meander along the bottom.
present tense: Anemones prey on unwary fish.
future tense: Anemones will prey on unwary fish.
present tense: Octopuses squirt ink.
future tense: Octopuses will squirt ink.

**Review Work** Write the past tense of each verb from the sentences.

**Draft Book** Write five sentences using verbs in the future tense. Put the helping word will in front of each verb. Underline the verbs with blue, including the word will.

38

**RW: Write swam, floated, sailed, meandered, preyed and squirted. DB: Answers will vary.**

**Page 39**

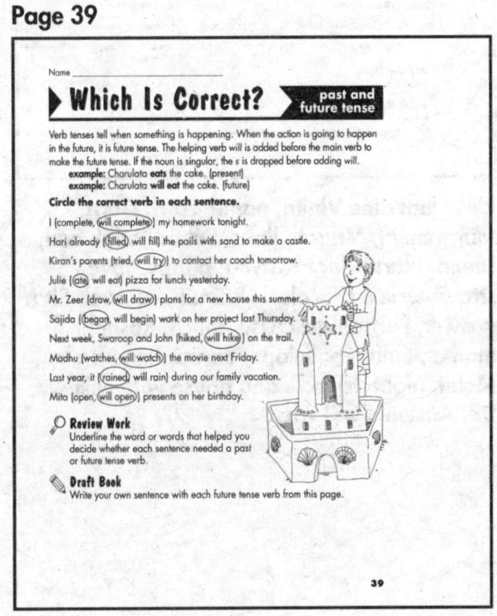

Name

# Which Is Correct?
past and future tense

Verb tenses tell when something is happening. When the action is going to happen in the future, it is future tense. The helping verb *will* is added before the main verb to make the future tense. If the noun is singular, the *s* is dropped before adding will.
**example:** Charulata **eats** the cake. (present)
**example:** Charulata **will eat** the cake. (future)

**Circle the correct verb in each sentence.**

I (complete, will complete) my homework tonight.
Hari already (filled, will fill) the pails with sand to make a castle.
Kiran's parents (tried, will try) to contact her coach tomorrow.
Julie (ate, will eat) pizza for lunch yesterday.
Mr. Zeer (drew, will draw) plans for a new house this summer.
Sajida (began, will begin) work on her project last Thursday.
Next week, Swaroop and John (hiked, will hike) on the trail.
Madhu (watches, will watch) the movie next Friday.
Last year, it (rained, will rain) during our family vacation.
Mita (open, will open) presents on her birthday.

**Review Work** Underline the word or words that helped you decide whether each sentence needed a past or future tense verb.

**Draft Book** Write your own sentence with each future tense verb from this page.

39

**Answer Key**

**Page 39 (cont.)**

**RW: Underline tonight, already, tomorrow, yesterday, this summer, last Thursday, next week, next Friday, last year and on her birthday. DB: Answers will vary.**

**Page 40**

Name ____

**Space Trip** — future tense

Verb tenses tell when something is happening. When the action is going to happen in the future, it is future tense. The helping verb *will* is added before the main verb to make the future tense. If the noun is singular, the s is dropped before adding will.
example: Sabu **raked** the lawn. (past)
example: Sabu **will rake** the lawn. (future)

**Write the correct future tense verb on the line.**

Irfan has plans to go into space.
A group (built) will build a huge rocket.
Technicians (checked) will check safety issues.
Irfan and his dad (mapped) will map the journey ahead of time.
Irfan and his friends (boarded) will board the rocket.
The announcer (counted) will count down to zero.
The rocket (exploded) will explode into orbit.
The crew (viewed) will view Earth from space.
They (observed) will observe comets and asteroids.
Irfan (kept) will keep a day-to-day journal.
Mahesh (recorded) will record space sounds.
Romila (photographed) will photograph interesting things.
Jyotsna (collected) will collect space dust.
They (returned) will return to Earth with many photos, recordings, items and stories.

**Review Work** Underline the nouns with yellow.
**Draft Book** Write about your own imaginary trip using future tense.

40

**RW: Underline Irfan, plans, space, group, rocket, technicians, issues, Irfan, dad, journey, time, Irfan, friends, rocket, announcer, zero, rocket, orbit, crew, Earth, space, comets, asteroids, Irfan, journal, Mahesh, sounds, Romila, things, Jyotsna, dust, Earth, photos, recordings, items and stories with yellow. DB: Answers will vary.**

**Page 41**

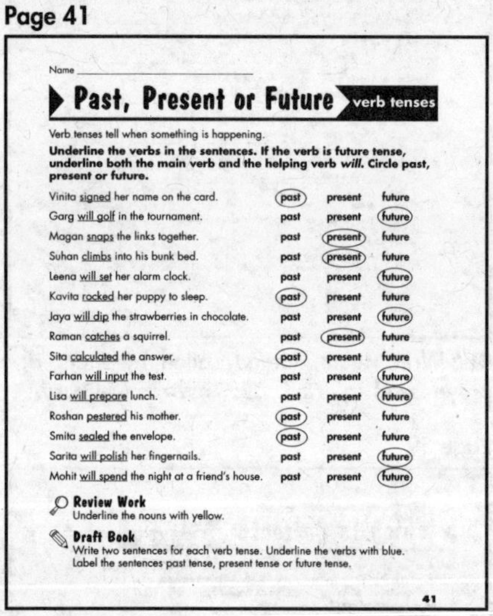
Name ____

**Past, Present or Future** — verb tenses

Verb tenses tell when something is happening.
**Underline the verbs in the sentences. If the verb is future tense, underline both the main verb and the helping verb *will*. Circle past, present or future.**

| | | | |
|---|---|---|---|
| Vinita signed her name on the card. | (past) | present | future |
| Garg will golf in the tournament. | past | present | (future) |
| Magan snaps the links together. | past | (present) | future |
| Suhan climbs into his bunk bed. | past | (present) | future |
| Leena will set her alarm clock. | past | present | (future) |
| Kavita rocked her puppy to sleep. | (past) | present | future |
| Jaya will dip the strawberries in chocolate. | past | present | (future) |
| Raman catches a squirrel. | past | (present) | future |
| Sita calculated the answer. | (past) | present | future |
| Farhan will input the test. | past | present | (future) |
| Lisa will prepare lunch. | past | present | (future) |
| Roshan pestered his mother. | (past) | present | future |
| Smita sealed the envelope. | (past) | present | future |
| Sarita will polish her fingernails. | past | present | (future) |
| Mohit will spend the night at a friend's house. | past | present | (future) |

**Review Work** Underline the nouns with yellow.
**Draft Book** Write two sentences for each verb tense. Underline the verbs with blue. Label the sentences past tense, present tense or future tense.

41

**RW: Underline Vinita, name, card, Garg, tournament, Magan, links, Suhan, bunk bed, Leena, alarm clock, Kavita, puppy, Jaya, strawberries, chocolate, Raman, squirrel, Sita, answer, Farhan, test, Lisa, lunch, Roshan, mother, Smita, envelope, Sarita, fingernails, Mohit, night, friend's and house with yellow. DB: Answers will vary.**

**Page 42**

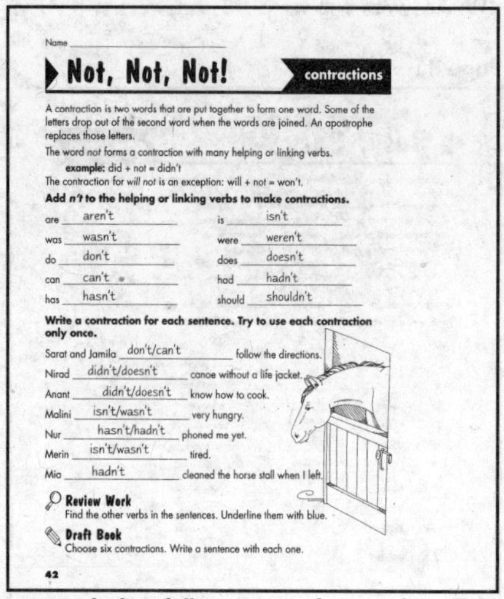
Name ____

**Not, Not, Not!** — contractions

A contraction is two words that are put together to form one word. Some of the letters drop out of the second word when the words are joined. An apostrophe replaces those letters.
The word *not* forms a contraction with many helping or linking verbs.
example: did + not = didn't
The contraction for *will not* is an exception: will + not = won't.

**Add *n't* to the helping or linking verbs to make contractions.**

| | | | |
|---|---|---|---|
| are | aren't | is | isn't |
| was | wasn't | were | weren't |
| do | don't | does | doesn't |
| can | can't | had | hadn't |
| has | hasn't | should | shouldn't |

**Write a contraction for each sentence. Try to use each contraction only once.**

Sarat and Jamila don't/can't follow the directions.
Nirad didn't/doesn't canoe without a life jacket.
Anant didn't/doesn't know how to cook.
Malini isn't/wasn't very hungry.
Nur hasn't/hadn't phoned me yet.
Merin isn't/wasn't tired.
Mia hadn't cleaned the horse stall when I left.

**Review Work** Find the other verbs in the sentences. Underline them with blue.
**Draft Book** Choose six contractions. Write a sentence with each one.

42

**RW: Underline follow, canoe, know, phoned, cleaned and left with blue. DB: Answers will vary.**

**Page 43**

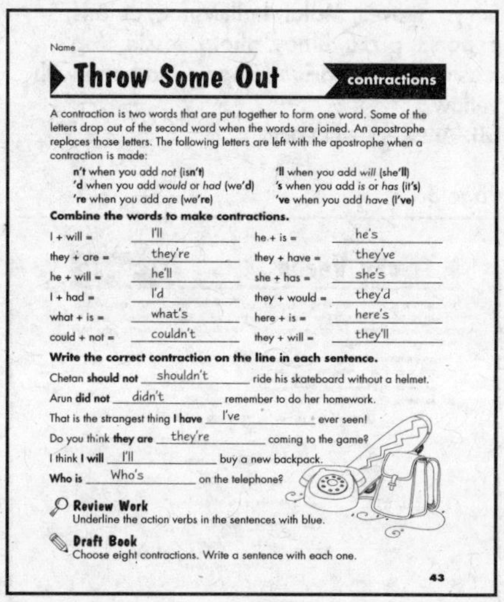
Name ____

**Throw Some Out** — contractions

A contraction is two words that are put together to form one word. Some of the letters drop out of the second word when the words are joined. An apostrophe replaces those letters. The following letters are left with the apostrophe when a contraction is made:
**n't** when you add *not* (isn't) — **'ll** when you add *will* (she'll)
**'d** when you add *would* or *had* (we'd) — **'s** when you add *is* or *has* (it's)
**'re** when you add *are* (we're) — **'ve** when you add *have* (I've)

**Combine the words to make contractions.**

| | | | |
|---|---|---|---|
| I + will = | I'll | he + is = | he's |
| they + are = | they're | they + have = | they've |
| he + will = | he'll | she + has = | she's |
| I + had = | I'd | they + would = | they'd |
| what + is = | what's | here + is = | here's |
| could + not = | couldn't | they + will = | they'll |

**Write the correct contraction on the line in each sentence.**

Chetan **should not** shouldn't ride his skateboard without a helmet.
Arun **did not** didn't remember to do her homework.
That is the strangest thing **I have** I've ever seen!
Do you think **they are** they're coming to the game?
I think **I will** I'll buy a new backpack.
**Who is** Who's on the telephone?

**Review Work** Underline the action verbs in the sentences with blue.
**Draft Book** Choose eight contractions. Write a sentence with each one.

43

**RW: Underline ride, remember, seen, coming and buy with blue. DB: Answers will vary.**

**Page 44**

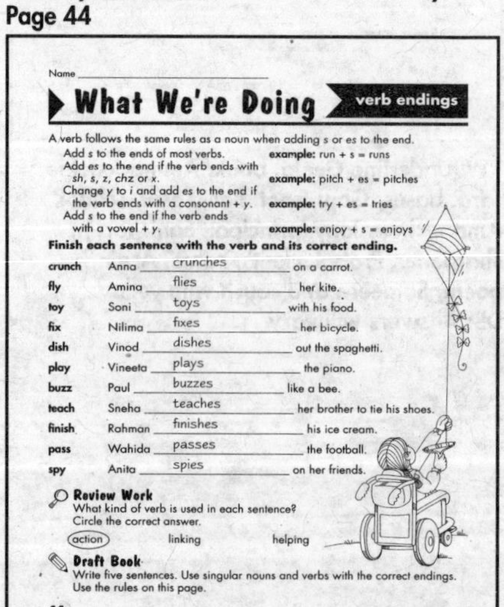
Name ____

**What We're Doing** — verb endings

A verb follows the same rules as a noun when adding *s* or *es* to the end.
Add *s* to the ends of most verbs. — example: run + s = runs
Add *es* to the end if the verb ends with *sh, s, z, chz* or *x*. — example: pitch + es = pitches
Change *y* to *i* and add *es* to the end if the verb ends with a consonant + *y*. — example: try + es = tries
Add *s* to the end if the verb ends with a vowel + *y*. — example: enjoy + s = enjoys

**Finish each sentence with the verb and its correct ending.**

| | | |
|---|---|---|
| crunch | Anna crunches | on a carrot. |
| fly | Amina flies | her kite. |
| toy | Soni toys | with his food. |
| fix | Nilima fixes | her bicycle. |
| dish | Vinod dishes | out the spaghetti. |
| play | Vineeta plays | the piano. |
| buzz | Paul buzzes | like a bee. |
| teach | Sneha teaches | her brother to tie his shoes. |
| finish | Rahman finishes | his ice cream. |
| pass | Wahida passes | the football. |
| spy | Anita spies | on her friends. |

**Review Work** What kind of verb is used in each sentence? Circle the correct answer.
(action) — linking — helping
**Draft Book** Write five sentences. Use singular nouns and verbs with the correct endings. Use the rules on this page.

44

**DB: Answers will vary.**

**Page 45**

Name ____

**Twilight** — noun and verb agreement

A singular noun uses a verb that has an *s* at the end.
example: The boy **climbs** the tree.
A plural noun uses a verb that does not have an *s* at the end.
example: The boys **climb** the tree.

**Circle the correct verb(s) in each sentence.**

Fluffy white clouds ((drift) drifts) along.
The sun (fade, (fades)) behind the horizon.
A dog (bound, (bounds)) into the yard.
The door (open, (opens)).
The boy (hear, (hears)) many sounds.
Buddy (run, (runs)) into the woods and Kamal (follow, (follows)).
Kamal (walk, (walks)) out after his dog, Buddy.
Owls ((call) calls) to one another.
Insects ((buzz) buzzes) and ((hum) hums).
Bullfrogs ((croak) croaks).
The two friends ((return) returns) home in soft darkness.
Stars ((twinkle) twinkles) in the sky.
Kamal (call, (calls)) quietly to Buddy.
Buddy (reenter, (reenters)) the house with Kamal.

**Review Work** Underline the nouns in the sentences with yellow.
**Draft Book** Choose five of the sentences. Rewrite each one so that the first noun becomes the opposite (singular or plural) of what it is now. Make sure the verb has the correct ending to agree with the new noun.

45

**RW: Underline clouds, sun, horizon, dog, yard, door, boy, sounds, Buddy, woods, Kamal, Kamal, dog, Buddy, owls, insects, bullfrogs, friends, home, darkness, stars, sky, Kamal, Buddy, Buddy, house and Kamal with yellow. DB: Answers will vary.**

**Page 46**

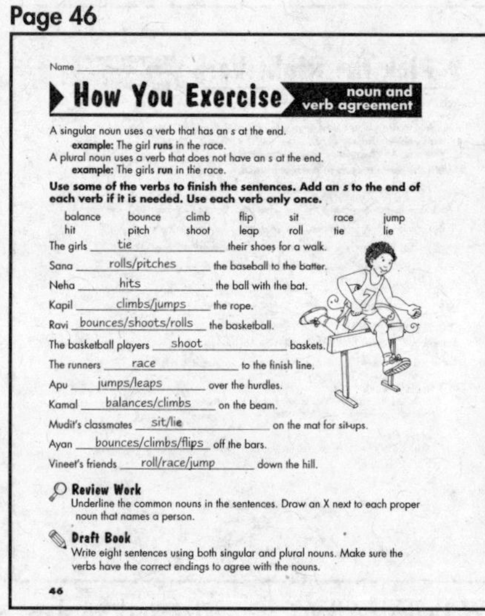
Name ____

**How You Exercise** — noun and verb agreement

A singular noun uses a verb that has an *s* at the end.
example: The girl **runs** in the race.
A plural noun uses a verb that does not have an *s* at the end.
example: The girls **run** in the race.

**Use some of the verbs to finish the sentences. Add an *s* to the end of each verb if it is needed. Use each verb only once.**

balance, bounce, climb, flip, sit, race, jump, hit, pitch, shoot, leap, roll, tie, lie

The girls tie their shoes for a walk.
Sana rolls/pitches the baseball to the batter.
Neha hits the ball with the bat.
Kapil climbs/jumps the rope.
Ravi bounces/shoots/rolls the basketball.
The basketball players shoot baskets.
The runners race to the finish line.
Apu jumps/leaps over the hurdles.
Kamal balances/climbs on the beam.
Mudit's classmates sit/lie on the mat for sit-ups.
Ayan bounces/climbs/flips off the bars.
Vineet's friends roll/race/jump down the hill.

**Review Work** Underline the common nouns in the sentences. Draw an X next to each proper noun that names a person.
**Draft Book** Write eight sentences using both singular and plural nouns. Make sure the verbs have the correct endings to agree with the nouns.

46

**RW: Underline girls, shoes, walk, baseball, batter, ball, bat, rope, basketball, players, baskets, runners, finish line, hurdles, beam, classmates, mat, sit-ups, bars, friends and hill. Draw an X next to Sana, Neha, Kapil, Ravi, Apu, Kamal, Mudit, Ayan and Vineet. DB: Answers will vary.**

**Answer Key**

Page 47

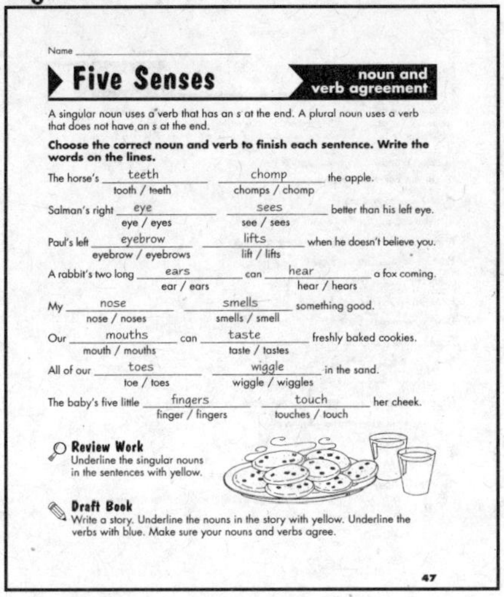

RW: Underline apple, eye, fox, sand and cheek with yellow.
DB: Answers will vary.

Page 48

RW: Underline Devan, package, ants, sandwich, mosquito, ear, cotton candy, Wahid, socks, shoes, bag, dalmatians, fire engine, Ram, scissors, paper, Jay, lemons, lemonade, Preeti, apple, Sumit and music with yellow. Underline opened, crawled, buzzes, is, has, rode, used, squeezed, ate and listened with blue.
DB: Answers will vary.

Page 49
Answers will vary.
RW: Underline Anna, grandmother, boots, phone, tissue, Bangalore, dog and pen with yellow. Underline held, shown, slept and run with blue. DB: Answers will vary.

Page 50
Answers will vary.

Page 51

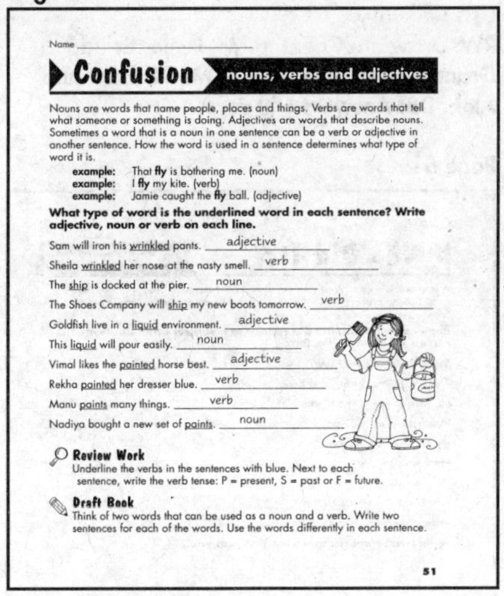

RW: Underline will iron, wrinkled, is docked, will ship, live, will pour, likes, painted, paints and bought with blue. 1. F 2. S 3. P 4. F 5. P 6. F 7. P 8. S 9. P 10. S
DB: Answers will vary.

Page 52
Draw lines to match unhappy/not happy, bicycle/cycle with two wheels, rewind/wind again, uncover/not cover, uninformed/not informed, prewritten/written before, bimonthly/every two months, unknown/not known and unicycle/cycle with one wheel. 1. not opened 2. washed before 3. every two weeks or two times a week
RW: Add uppercase letters and ending punctuation. DB: Answers will vary.

Page 53

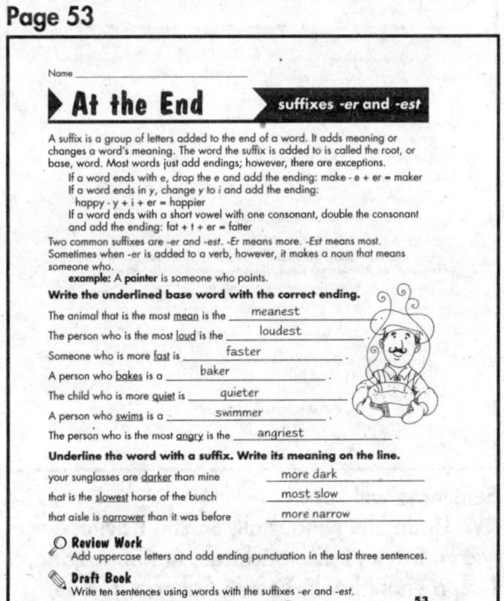

RW: Add uppercase letters and ending punctuation. DB: Answers will vary.

Page 54

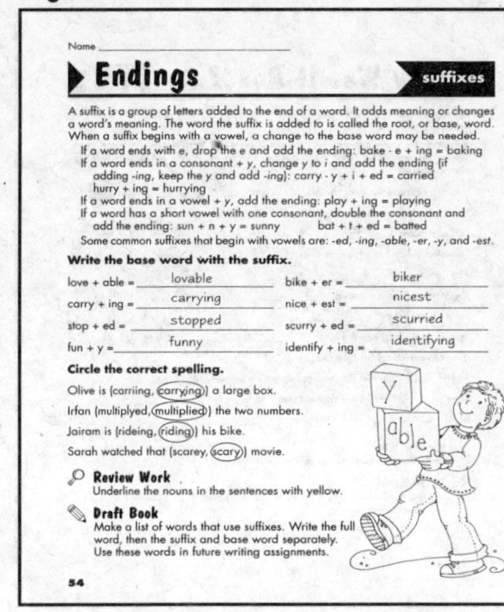

RW: Underline Olive, box, Irfan, numbers, Jairam, bike, Sarah and movie with yellow.
DB: Answers will vary.

Page 55

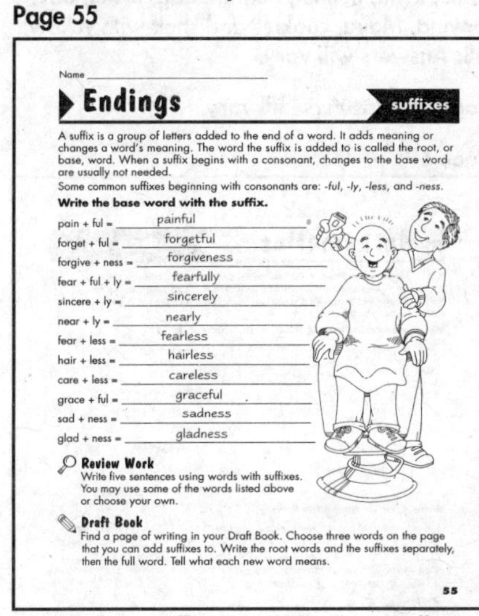

RW: Answers will vary. DB: Answers will vary.

Page 56

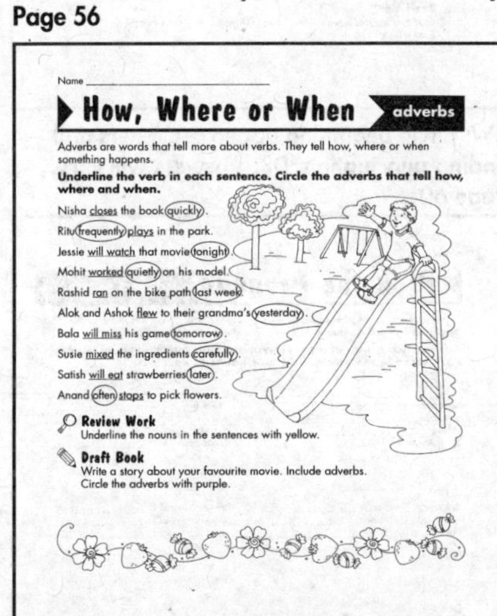

RW: Underline Nisha, book, Ritu, park, Jessie, movie, Mohit, model, Rashid, path, Alok, Ashok, grandma's, Bala, game, Susie, ingredients, Satish, strawberries, Anand and flowers with yellow. DB: Answers will vary.

## Answer Key

### Page 57

Name ____________

**How Was it Done?** adverbs

Adverbs are words that tell more about verbs. They tell how, where or when something happens.

**What does each adverb tell about the verb? Write *how, where* or *when* on each line. Draw an arrow to the verb the adverb is telling more about.**

Lata worked **smarter** than she had in the past. how
Nihar swam **through** the channel. where
Arti jogs **daily**. when
The wind **wildly** blew the branches. how
Rita complained **loudly**. how
The storm will be here **soon**. when
Nita **never** cheats. when
Suraiah **cheerfully** sets the table. how
Irfan **always** wears his bike helmet. when
Suman rubbed the wet dog **vigorously** with a towel. how
After playing all day, Govind went **inside** to relax. where
Maya put the cookies **up** on the shelf. where

**Review Work** Underline the nouns in the sentences with yellow.

**Draft Book** Write a story about a thunderstorm you remember. Include adverbs. Circle the adverbs with purple.

57

**RW: Underline Lata, past, Nihar, channel, Arti, wind, branches, Rita, storm, Nita, Suraiah, table, Irfan, helmet, Suman, dog, towel, day, Govind, Maya, cookies and shelf with yellow. DB: Answers will vary.**

### Page 58: Answers will vary.

### Page 59

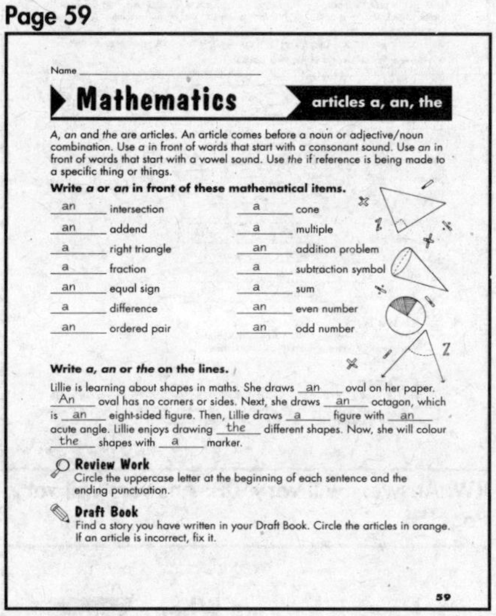
Name ____________

**Mathematics** articles a, an, the

A, an and the are articles. An article comes before a noun or adjective/noun combination. Use *a* in front of words that start with a consonant sound. Use *an* in front of words that start with a vowel sound. Use *the* if reference is being made to a specific thing or things.

**Write *a* or *an* in front of these mathematical items.**

| | | | |
|---|---|---|---|
| an | intersection | a | cone |
| an | addend | a | multiple |
| a | right triangle | an | addition problem |
| a | fraction | a | subtraction symbol |
| an | equal sign | a | sum |
| a | difference | an | even number |
| an | ordered pair | an | odd number |

**Write *a, an* or *the* on the lines.**

Lillie is learning about shapes in maths. She draws an oval on her paper. An oval has no corners or sides. Next, she draws an octagon, which is an eight-sided figure. Then, Lillie draws a figure with an acute angle. Lillie enjoys drawing the different shapes. Now, she will colour the shapes with a marker.

**Review Work** Circle the uppercase letter at the beginning of each sentence and the ending punctuation.

**Draft Book** Find a story you have written in your Draft Book. Circle the articles in orange. If an article is incorrect, fix it.

59

**RW: Circle beginning uppercase letters and ending punctuation. DB: Answers will vary.**

### Page 60

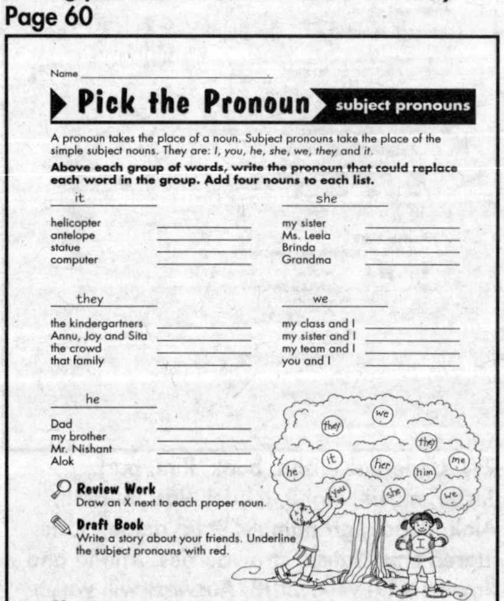
Name ____________

**Pick the Pronoun** subject pronouns

A pronoun takes the place of a noun. Subject pronouns take the place of the simple subject nouns. They are: *I, you, he, she, we, they* and *it*.

**Above each group of words, write the pronoun that could replace each word in the group. Add four nouns to each list.**

it: helicopter, antelope, statue, computer

she: my sister, Ms. Leela, Brinda, Grandma

they: the kindergartners, Annu, Joy and Sita, the crowd, that family

we: my class and I, my sister and I, my team and I, you and I

he: Dad, my brother, Mr. Nishant, Alok



**Review Work** Draw an X next to each proper noun.

**Draft Book** Write a story about your friends. Underline the subject pronouns with red.

60

### Page 60 (cont.)

**Lists will vary.**
**RW: Draw an X next to Ms. Leela, Brinda, Grandma, Annu, Joy, Sita, Mr. Nishant and Alok. DB: Answers will vary.**

### Page 61

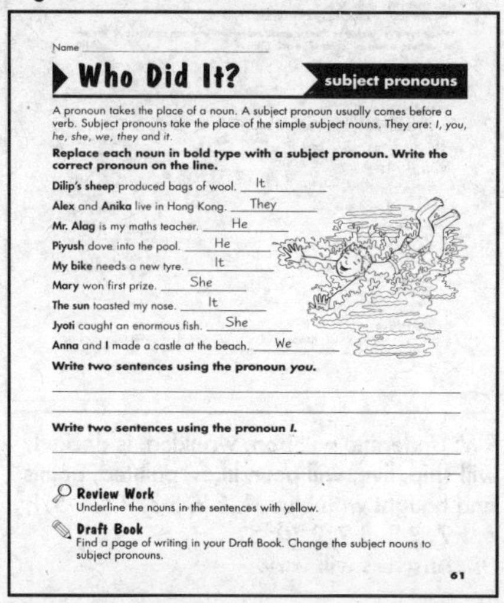
Name ____________

**Who Did It?** subject pronouns

A pronoun takes the place of a noun. A subject pronoun usually comes before a verb. Subject pronouns take the place of the simple subject nouns. They are: *I, you, he, she, we, they* and *it*.

**Replace each noun in bold type with a subject pronoun. Write the correct pronoun on the line.**

**Dilip's sheep** produced bags of wool. It
**Alex** and **Anika** live in Hong Kong. They
**Mr. Alag** is my maths teacher. He
**Piyush** dove into the pool. He
**My bike** needs a new tyre. It
**Mary** won first prize. She
**The sun** toasted my nose. It
**Jyoti** caught an enormous fish. She
**Anna** and **I** made a castle at the beach. We

**Write two sentences using the pronoun *you*.**

**Write two sentences using the pronoun *I*.**

**Review Work** Underline the nouns in the sentences with yellow.

**Draft Book** Find a page of writing in your Draft Book. Change the subject nouns to subject pronouns.

61

**Sentences will vary.**
**RW: Underline sheep, bags, wool, Alex, Anika, Hong Kong, Mr. Alag, teacher, Piyush, pool, bike, tyre, Mary, prize, sun, nose, Jyoti, fish, Anna, castle and beach with yellow. DB: Answers will vary.**

### Page 62

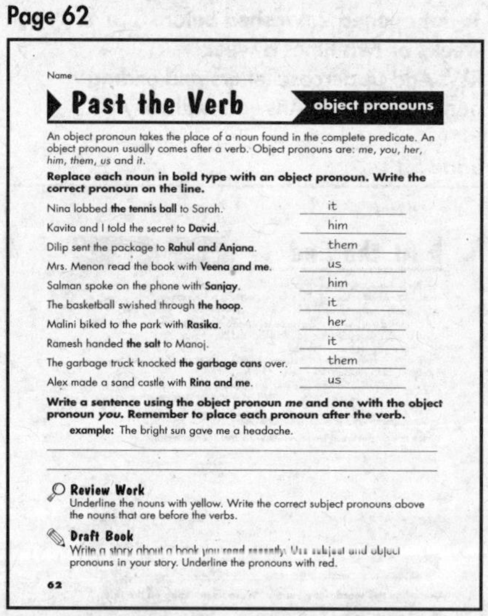
Name ____________

**Past the Verb** object pronouns

An object pronoun takes the place of a noun found in the complete predicate. An object pronoun usually comes after a verb. Object pronouns are: *me, you, her, him, them, us* and *it*.

**Replace each noun in bold type with an object pronoun. Write the correct pronoun on the line.**

Nina lobbed **the tennis ball** to Sarah. it
Kavita and I told the secret to **David**. him
Dilip sent the package to **Rahul and Anjana**. them
Mrs. Menon read the book with **Veena and me**. us
Salman spoke on the phone with **Sanjay**. him
The basketball swished through **the hoop**. it
Malini biked to the park with **Rasika**. her
Ramesh handed **the salt** to Manoj. it
The garbage truck knocked **the garbage cans** over. them
Alex made a sand castle with **Rina and me**. us

**Write a sentence using the object pronoun *me* and one with the object pronoun *you*. Remember to place each pronoun after the verb.**
**example:** The bright sun gave me a headache.

**Review Work** Underline the nouns with yellow. Write the correct subject pronouns above the nouns that are before the verbs.

**Draft Book** Write a story about a book you read recently. Use subject and object pronouns in your story. Underline the pronouns with red.

62

**Sentences will vary.**
**RW: Underline Nina, ball, Sarah, Kavita, secret, David, Dilip, package, Rahul, Anjana, Mrs. Menon, book, Veena, Salman, phone, Sanjay, basketball, hoop, Malini, park, Rasika, Ramesh, salt, Manoj, truck, cans, Alex, sand castle and Rina with yellow. 1. She 2. She 3. He 4. She 5. He 6. It 7. She 8. He 9. It 10. He DB: Answers will vary.**

### Page 63

Name ____________

**I or Me?** pronouns

Pronouns take the place of nouns. Subject pronouns take the place of subject nouns. Object pronouns take the place of predicate nouns. A subject pronoun usually comes before a verb. An object pronoun usually comes after a verb.
subject pronouns: I, you, he, she, we, they, it
object pronouns: me, you, her, him, them, us, it

**Circle the correct pronoun.**

(I, Me) went to the library.
Can you come to the pool with (we, us)?
(He, Him) helped (I, me) put up the poster.
Hannah delivered the package to (they, them).
(She, Her) caught a butterfly.
(We, Us) will build a tree fort.
Did (he, him) get a turn?
Jeet threw the ball to (he, him).
Diya likes soccer, but (she, her) likes golf better.
Mr. Parashar checked out the book to (she, her).
(She, Her) will put the stamp on the envelope. Then, (she, her) will mail it.
(We, Us) went with (she, her) to the store.

**Review Work** Draw a X next to each proper noun.

**Draft Book** Find a page of writing in your Draft Book. Underline the pronouns with red. Make corrections where necessary.

63

**RW: Draw an X next to Hannah, Jeet, Diya and Mr. Parashar. DB: Answers will vary.**

### Page 64

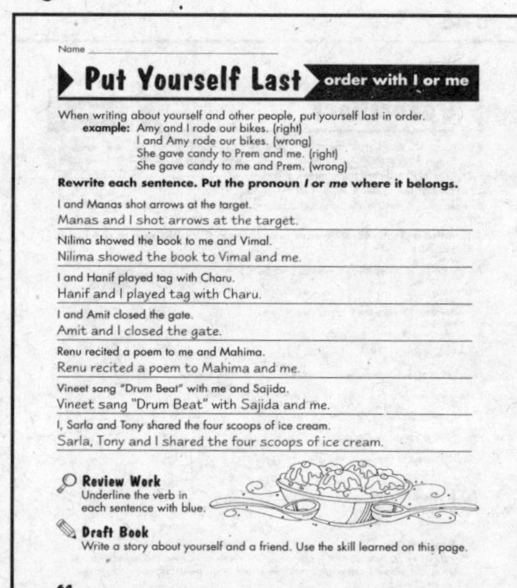
Name ____________

**Put Yourself Last** order with I or me

When writing about yourself and other people, put yourself last in order.
**example:** Amy and I rode our bikes. (right)
I and Amy rode our bikes. (wrong)
She gave candy to Prem and me. (right)
She gave candy to me and Prem. (wrong)

**Rewrite each sentence. Put the pronoun *I* or *me* where it belongs.**

I and Manas shot arrows at the target.
Manas and I shot arrows at the target.
Nilima showed the book to me and Vimal.
Nilima showed the book to Vimal and me.
I and Hanif played tag with Charu.
Hanif and I played tag with Charu.
I and Amit closed the gate.
Amit and I closed the gate.
Renu recited a poem to me and Mahima.
Renu recited a poem to Mahima and me.
Vineet sang "Drum Beat" with me and Sajida.
Vineet sang "Drum Beat" with Sajida and me.
I, Sarla and Tony shared the four scoops of ice cream.
Sarla, Tony and I shared the four scoops of ice cream.

**Review Work** Underline the verb in each sentence with blue.

**Draft Book** Write a story about yourself and a friend. Use the skill learned on this page.

64

**RW: Underline shot, showed, played, closed, recited, sang and shared with blue. DB: Answers will vary.**

### Page 65

Name ____________

**My Bike Bumped His Bike** possessive pronouns

Possessive pronouns take the place of possessive nouns. They are: *my, your, his, her, its, our* and *their*. The possessive pronoun *its* does not have an apostrophe.

**Write the correct possessive pronoun on each line.**

His (Jatin's) chair bumped Anil.
Latika broke his (Bijoy's) glasses.
Rahul borrowed our (Mira's and my) markers.
We tossed their (the dogs') slimy bones.
Its (The phone's) ring is loud.
Our (My family's) car bumped our mailbox.
Those blueberries stained their (Tarun's and Amy's) shirts.
His (Sohan's) computer downloaded that message.

**Write a sentence for each of the following pronouns: *my* and *your*.**

**Review Work** Underline the verb in each sentence with blue.

**Draft Book** Write 10 sentences using possessive pronouns.

65

**Answer Key**

**Page 65 (cont.)**
Sentences will vary.
RW: Underline bumped, broke, borrowed, tossed, is, bumped, stained and downloaded with blue. DB: Answers will vary.

**Page 66**

Name ____________
**Mine, Ours, Theirs** — possessive pronouns
Possessive pronouns take the place of possessive nouns. They can be used before a noun or alone. The possessive pronoun its does not have an apostrophe.
before a noun: my, your, his, her, its, our, their
alone: mine, yours, his, hers, its, ours, theirs
**Circle the correct pronoun.**
Jan wants (my, mine) paper.
That plant is (her, hers).
(Our, Ours) house is the white one with blue trim.
Bring (your, yours) swimsuit along.
(Their, Theirs) car was parked next to the building.
Piyush has (our, his) own paints, but he wants to borrow (her, hers).
Dad will buy me a swing set like (their, theirs).
That ice cream cone you ate was (my, mine).
We will bring (our, ours) lunches on the field trip.
(Her, Hers) scissors dropped on the floor.
That team lost their bat, so they borrowed (our, ours).
Aruna has a bike, but she wants to use (your, yours).
**Review Work** Write the verb tense beside each sentence: P = present, S = past or F = future.
**Draft Book** Write 10 sentences using possessive pronouns. Use each possessive pronoun at least once.
66

RW: 1. P 2. P 3. P 4. P 5. S 6. P 7. F 8. S 9. F 10. S 11. S 12. P DB: Answers will vary.

**Page 67**

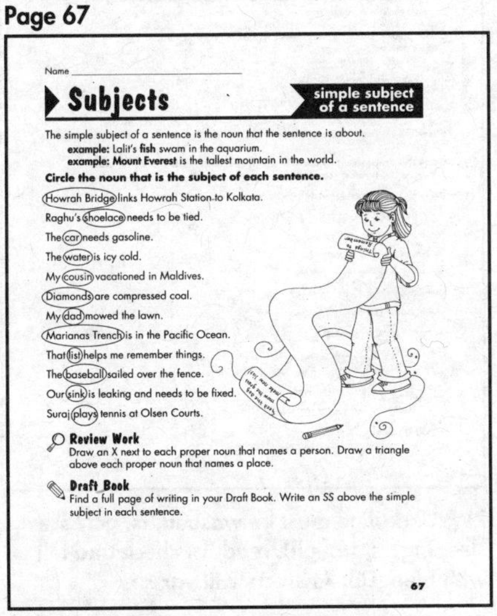
Name ____________
**Subjects** — simple subject of a sentence
The simple subject of a sentence is the noun that the sentence is about.
example: Lalit's fish swam in the aquarium.
example: Mount Everest is the tallest mountain in the world.
**Circle the noun that is the subject of each sentence.**
Howrah Bridge links Howrah Station to Kolkata.
Raghu's shoelace needs to be tied.
The car needs gasoline.
The water is icy cold.
My cousin vacationed in Maldives.
Diamonds are compressed coal.
My dad mowed the lawn.
Marianas Trench is in the Pacific Ocean.
That list helps me remember things.
The baseball sailed over the fence.
Our sink is leaking and needs to be fixed.
Suraj plays tennis at Olsen Courts.
**Review Work** Draw an X next to each proper noun that names a person. Draw a triangle above each proper noun that names a place.
**Draft Book** Find a full page of writing in your Draft Book. Write an SS above the simple subject in each sentence.
67

RW: Draw an X next to Raghu and Suraj. Draw a triangle above Howrah Bridge, Kolkata, Maldives, Marianas Trench, Pacific Ocean and Olsen Courts. DB: Answers will vary.

**Page 68**
Answers will vary.
RW: Underline people, dates, trees, sky, fruit, water and game with yellow.
DB: Answers will vary.

**Page 69**

Name ____________
**Keep It Simple** — simple predicate
The simple predicate is the verb that tells what someone or something is doing.
example: Imran kicked the football for the winning goal.
**Underline each simple predicate.**
Lina scrunched up her nose.
Deepak bounced on his bed.
Lisa rustled the bag of chips.
Anil breezed through the entryway.
The swan paddled in the pond.
The dog tripped over my foot.
Arun dated his paper.
Mrs. Tara indented the paragraph.
The pudding splattered all over the floor.
Julie scurried to get her work done.
The dancers leaped across the stage.
Manas created a new cookie.
Anil ended his story.
**Review Work** Underline the nouns with yellow.
**Draft Book** Use one sentence on this page in a story. Underline the simple predicates in your story with blue.
69

RW: Underline Lina, nose, Deepak, bed, Lisa, bag, chips, Anil, entryway, swan, pond, dog, foot, Arun, paper, Mrs. Tara, paragraph, pudding, floor, Julie, work, dancers, stage, Manas, cookie, Anil and story with yellow. DB: Answers will vary.

**Page 70**

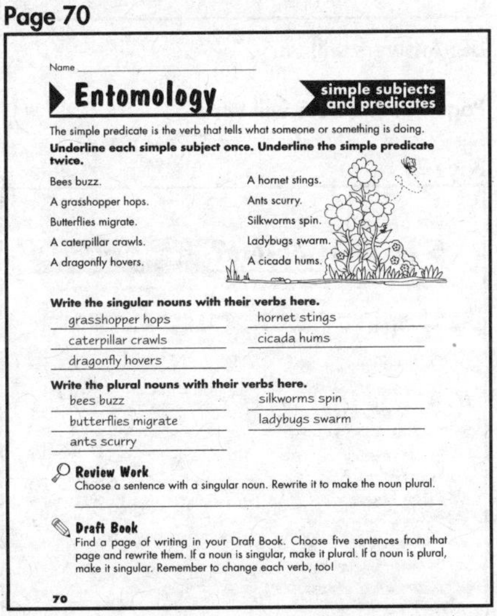
Name ____________
**Entomology** — simple subjects and predicates
The simple predicate is the verb that tells what someone or something is doing.
**Underline each simple subject once. Underline the simple predicate twice.**
Bees buzz. — A hornet stings.
A grasshopper hops. — Ants scurry.
Butterflies migrate. — Silkworms spin.
A caterpillar crawls. — Ladybugs swarm.
A dragonfly hovers. — A cicada hums.
**Write the singular nouns with their verbs here.**
grasshopper hops — hornet stings
caterpillar crawls — cicada hums
dragonfly hovers
**Write the plural nouns with their verbs here.**
bees buzz — silkworms spin
butterflies migrate — ladybugs swarm
ants scurry
**Review Work** Choose a sentence with a singular noun. Rewrite it to make the noun plural.
**Draft Book** Find a page of writing in your Draft Book. Choose five sentences from that page and rewrite them. If a noun is singular, make it plural. If a noun is plural, make it singular. Remember to change each verb, too!
70

RW: Answers will vary. DB: Answers will vary.

**Page 71**

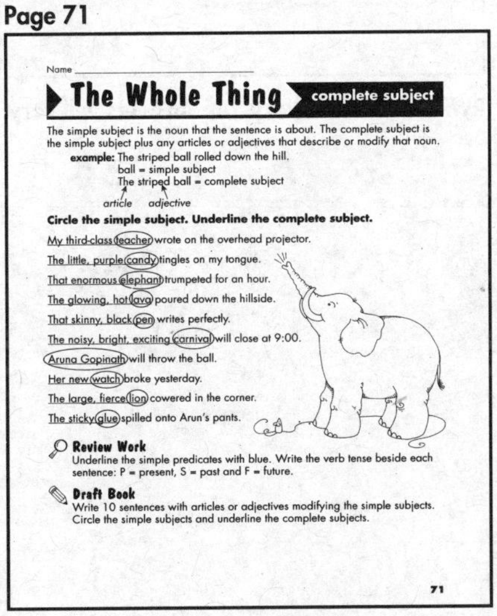
Name ____________
**The Whole Thing** — complete subject
The simple subject is the noun that the sentence is about. The complete subject is the simple subject plus any articles or adjectives that describe or modify that noun.
example: The striped ball rolled down the hill.
ball = simple subject
The striped ball = complete subject
article adjective
**Circle the simple subject. Underline the complete subject.**
My third-class teacher wrote on the overhead projector.
The little, purple candy tingles on my tongue.
That enormous elephant trumpeted for an hour.
The glowing, hot lava poured down the hillside.
That skinny, black pen writes perfectly.
The noisy, bright, exciting carnival will close at 9:00.
Aruna Gopinath will throw the ball.
Her new watch broke yesterday.
The large, fierce lion cowered in the corner.
The sticky glue spilled onto Arun's pants.
**Review Work** Underline the simple predicates with blue. Write the verb tense beside each sentence: P = present, S = past and F = future.
**Draft Book** Write 10 sentences with articles or adjectives modifying the simple subjects. Circle the simple subjects and underline the complete subjects.
71

**Page 71 (cont.)**
RW: Underline wrote, tingles, trumpeted, poured, writes, close, throw, broke, cowered and spilled with blue. 1. S 2. P 3. S 4. S 5. P 6. F 7. F 8. S 9. S 10. S
DB: Answers will vary.

**Page 72**

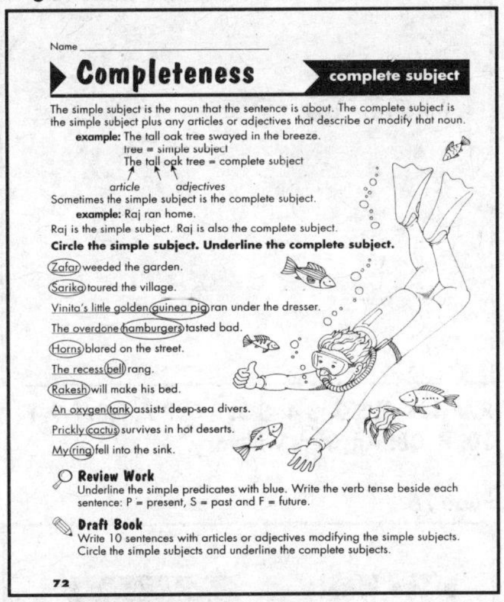
Name ____________
**Completeness** — complete subject
The simple subject is the noun that the sentence is about. The complete subject is the simple subject plus any articles or adjectives that describe or modify that noun.
example: The tall oak tree swayed in the breeze.
tree = simple subject
The tall oak tree = complete subject
article adjectives
Sometimes the simple subject is the complete subject.
example: Raj ran home.
Raj is the simple subject. Raj is also the complete subject.
**Circle the simple subject. Underline the complete subject.**
Zafar weeded the garden.
Sarika toured the village.
Vinita's little golden guinea pig ran under the dresser.
The overdone hamburgers tasted bad.
Horns blared on the street.
The recess bell rang.
Rakesh will make his bed.
An oxygen tank assists deep-sea divers.
Prickly cactus survives in hot deserts.
My ring fell into the sink.
**Review Work** Underline the simple predicates with blue. Write the verb tense beside each sentence: P = present, S = past and F = future.
**Draft Book** Write 10 sentences with articles or adjectives modifying the simple subjects. Circle the simple subjects and underline the complete subjects.
72

RW: Underline weeded, toured, ran, tasted, blared, rang, make, assists, survives and fell with blue. 1. S 2. S 3. S 4. S 5. S 6. S 7. F 8. P 9. P 10. S DB: Answers will vary.

**Page 73**

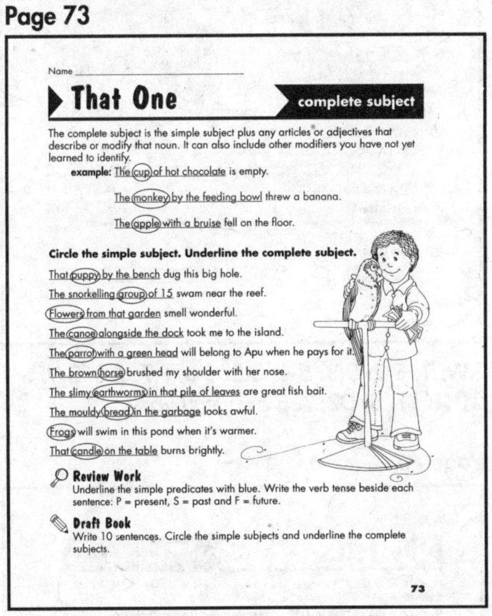
Name ____________
**That One** — complete subject
The complete subject is the simple subject plus any articles or adjectives that describe or modify that noun. It can also include other modifiers you have not yet learned to identify.
example: The cup of hot chocolate is empty.
The monkey by the feeding bowl threw a banana.
The apple with a bruise fell on the floor.
**Circle the simple subject. Underline the complete subject.**
That puppy by the bench dug this big hole.
The snorkelling group of 15 swam near the reef.
Flowers from that garden smell wonderful.
The canoe alongside the dock took me to the island.
The parrot with a green head will belong to Apu when he pays for it.
The brown horse brushed my shoulder with her nose.
The slimy earthworms in that pile of leaves are great fish bait.
The mouldy bread in the garbage looks awful.
Frogs will swim in this pond when it's warmer.
That candle on the table burns brightly.
**Review Work** Underline the simple predicates with blue. Write the verb tense beside each sentence: P = present, S = past and F = future.
**Draft Book** Write 10 sentences. Circle the simple subjects and underline the complete subjects.
73

RW: Underline dug, swam, smell, took, belong, brushed, are, looks, swim and burns with blue. 1. S 2. S 3. P 4. S 5. F 6. S 7. P 8. P 9. F 10. P
DB: Answers will vary.

## Answer Key

### Page 74

Name

**Here We Go** — complete predicate

The simple predicate is the verb that tells what someone or something is doing. The complete predicate is the simple predicate plus any helping or linking verbs and any adverbs that describe or modify the verb.

**example:** The ball will roll smoothly.
roll = simple predicate
will roll smoothly = complete predicate
helping verb adverb

**Circle the simple predicate. Underline the complete predicate twice.**

Sanat often reads quickly.
The snow frequently fell rapidly.
The rain pounded loudly last night.
The wet dog shook vigorously.
An ant may have wandered around yesterday.
Nikhil never screams loudly.
That koala will eat constantly.
That lion could lunge immediately.
Lina may finish tonight.
Those tennis shoes smell awful.

**Review Work**
Identify the verb tense of each sentence. Write the verb tense beside each sentence: P = present, S = past and F = future.

**Draft Book**
Write 10 sentences with helping or linking verbs and adverbs modifying the simple predicates. Circle the simple predicates and underline the complete predicates twice.

74

**RW: 1. P 2. S 3. S 4. S 5. S 6. P 7. F 8. F 9. F 10. P DB: Answers will vary.**

### Page 75

Name

**The Whole** — complete predicate

The complete predicate is the simple predicate plus any helping or linking verbs, any adverbs, and any other words that tell where, when, why or how the verb happens. If the words are not part of the complete subject, they are included in the complete predicate.

**example:** Sujit will bike to the beach.
The big red apple fell to the ground.
Sona played with her brother.

**Circle the simple predicate. Underline the complete predicate twice.**

The glass of milk spilled onto Hira's shoes.
Five tiny owlets hooted softly for a meal.
Chandu and Anita guarded the soccer goals.
Amrit filled the bird feeder last week.
The raccoons destroyed the garden.
The hen will gobble up any feed it finds.
Ziyad wandered aimlessly through the toy store.
Niraj quickly subtracted a page of numbers.
Roshan carefully sewed the button on his jacket.
Our family will attend the play next Tuesday.
A spider dangled above our heads.

**Review Work**
Identify the verb tense of each sentence. Write the verb tense beside each sentence: P = present, S = past and F = future.

**Draft Book**
Write 10 sentences with helping or linking verbs and adverbs modifying the simple predicates. Circle the simple predicates and underline the complete predicates twice.

75

**RW: 1. S 2. S 3. S 4. S 5. S 6. F 7. S 8. S 9. S 10. F 11. S DB: Answers will vary.**

### Page 76

Name

**Do Tell** — complete subjects and predicates

The complete subject tells who or what the sentence is about. The complete predicate tells what the someone or something is doing.

**Underline the complete subject once. Underline the complete predicate twice.**

The noisy movie prevented Udip from working.
The box of tissues emptied quickly.
The old, rusty swing continues to be the kids' favourite.
Pradeep loads the back of the truck with plants.
Many shiny marbles scattered across the tile floor.
Many important men signed the Declaration of Independence.
Few tomato plants survived the dog's digging.
The steep cliff towered above the river.
The remote-controlled car raced along the pavement.
The giant toad devoured many insects.
The tape secured the picture to the wall.

**Review Work**
Write an SS above the simple subject in each sentence. Circle the simple predicates.

**Draft Book**
Locate a page of writing in your Draft Book. Underline each complete subject once. Underline each complete predicate twice.

76

### Page 76 (cont.)

**RW: Write an SS above movie, box, swing, Pradeep, marbles, men, plants, cliff, car, toad and tape. Circle prevented, emptied, continues, loads, scattered, signed, survived, towered, raced, devoured and secured.**
**DB: Answers will vary.**

### Page 77

Name

**Star or X** — complete sentences

A sentence needs one complete subject and one complete predicate to be a sentence.
**example:** Jan has a dog. = sentence
complete subject complete predicate
a dog = not a sentence

A sentence can be long or short.
**example:** Jan walks.
complete subject complete predicate
**example:** The tiny little bird with the broken wing ← complete subject
finally flew out the door and into the backyard. ← complete predicate

**If the group of words is a sentence, put a star in the box. Underline the complete subject once. Underline the complete predicate twice. If the group of words is not a sentence, put an X in the box.**

| | |
|---|---|
| X The old yellow lion in the cage. | ☆ Carrots are healthy. |
| X Walking through the quiet hallway. | ☆ That butterfly is beautiful. |
| X Many little. | ☆ Jay closed it. |
| ☆ The strawberries are tasty. | ☆ Jessie walks to school. |
| X Are very large. | X Going here? |
| X In that really scary house. | X The woods are. |
| ☆ Camp is fun. | X This bubble gum. |

**Review Work**
Write the linking verbs used in the groups of words from above.
are is

**Draft Book**
Make complete sentences using each group of words that has an X in the box.

77

**DB: Answers will vary.**

**Page 78: Answers will vary.**

### Page 79

Name

**Is it Complete?** — complete sentences

A group of words needs one complete subject and one complete predicate to be a sentence.

**If the group of words is a sentence, put a star in the box. Underline the complete subject once and the complete predicate twice. If the group of words is not a sentence, put an X in the box.**

The elephant is charging ☆
Raji has three adorable kittens ☆
John coloured the frog green ☆
That pair of scissors is sharp ☆
Did Sam collect the money ☆
Should this bike X
Can Renuka go swimming ☆
Of red and blue paper X
Moaning and groaning X
The bluebird swooped down to grab an insect ☆
Will bats fly in the backyard tonight ☆
Prem's umbrella in the old bucket X

**Review Work**
Write a complete sentence with each phrase with an X in its box.

**Draft Book**
Find a full page of writing in your Draft Book. Circle any groups of words that are not complete sentences and rewrite them so that they are complete.

79

**RW: Answers will vary. DB: Answers will vary.**

### Page 80

Name

**Noun Modifiers** — prepositions

A preposition is a word that relates a noun to other words in the sentence. It can give more information as well as tell location (where a noun is), direction (where a noun is going) or time (when a noun happens). Some common prepositions are: *by, from, to, in, in front of, next to, of, under* and *with*. The preposition must modify, or give more information about, the noun in the sentence, not the verb.

**Circle the prepositions. Underline the nouns they are modifying.**

Madhu would like a cup of hot chocolate.
The car next to the restaurant is ours.
Fida found her pencil under the couch.
The cookies in the jar are delicious.
The letter from my grandma came last night.
The seat in the middle is John's.
Keerti bought the goldfish with five black spots.
The bump in front of your sled will send you sailing.
The paper under the couch needs to be picked up.
The kittens with red collars are Manju's.
Sudeep brought a bag of potato chips.
Varun's skates are the ones with fluorescent orange wheels.
Gopi is painting the window by the ladder.
Manohar wants a piece of pie.

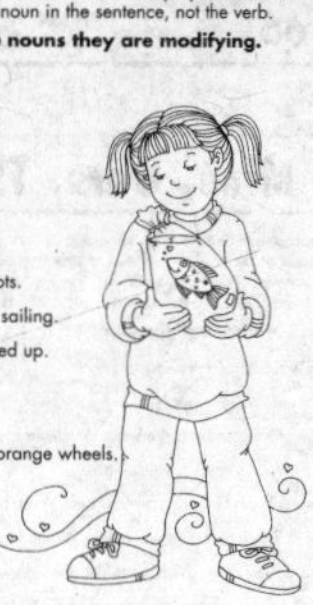

**Review Work**
Underline the verbs in the sentences with blue.

**Draft Book**
Write a sentence for each preposition above.

80

**RW: Underline would like, is, found, are, came, is, bought, will send, needs, are, brought, are, is painting and wants with blue.**
**DB: Answers will vary.**

### Page 81

Name

**Tell Me Which One** — prepositions

A preposition is a word that relates a noun to other words in the sentence. It can give more information as well as tell location (where a noun is), direction (where a noun is going) or time (when a noun happens). A preposition begins a phrase called a prepositional phrase.

noun modified
Megha drinks a cup of warm tea.
preposition prepositional phrase

Prepositions include: *by, from, to, in, in front of, next to, of, under* and *with*. The preposition must modify, or give more information about, the noun in the sentence, not the verb.

**Circle the preposition. Underline the prepositional phrase. Draw an arrow to the noun it modifies.**

The sweater with red stripes must be washed.
The student in the blue jacket is Pranesh.
Please get the pencil by the book.
The bats in the attic are sleeping.
The sandwich in that bag is mouldy.
Malati bought a doll with brown hair.
Farhan read a chapter from that book.
That desk next to mine is messy.
Check the atlas in the bookcase.
The bowl with cereal in it fell off the counter.

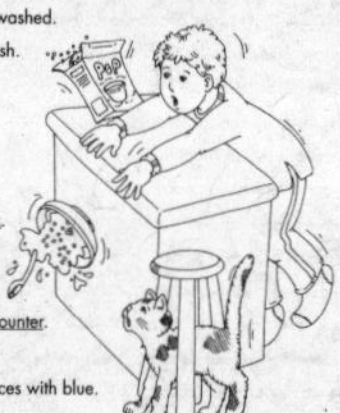

**Review Work**
Underline the verbs in the sentences with blue.

**Draft Book**
Write a sentence for each preposition above.

81

**RW: Underline must be washed, is, get, are sleeping, is, bought, read, is, check and fell with blue. DB: Answers will vary.**

### Page 82

Name

**We Sound the Same** — homophones

Homophones are words that sound alike but are spelt differently and have different meanings.

**Write the correct homophone on the line.**

**threw:** verb, past tense of throw **through:** between, from one side to another
Ria walked through the door.
Purnima looked through the window.
Anjali threw the winning pass.

**sent:** verb, past tense of send **scent:** a smell **cent:** unit of money
The scent of that flower is faint.
Mr. Hari sent Anila to the office.
This penny is worth one cent.

**its:** possessive pronoun **it's:** contraction for it is
It's very hot outside.
The class has its own drinking fountain.
Mrinal thinks it's too cold to go in the pool.
Its place is on that shelf.

**whole:** entire **hole:** part missing
The whole class is going on a field trip.
Charumati wanted the whole apple.
There is a hole in this sock.

**Review Work**
Underline the nouns with yellow.

**Draft Book**
Choose a pair of homophones. Write two sentences with each word.

82

**Answer Key**

**Page 82 (cont.)**

**RW: Underline Rita, door, Purnima, window, Anjali, pass, flower, Mr. Hari, Anilu, office, cent, penny, outside, class, fountain, Mrinal, pool, place, shelf, class, field trip, Charumati, apple, hole and sock with yellow.**
**DB: Answers will vary.**

**Page 83**

Name ____________

**We Sound the Same** homophones

Homophones are words that sound alike but are spelt differently and have different meanings.
**Write the correct homophone on the line.**

**no:** antonym of yes **know:** verb, to understand

No, you may not have any candy before dinner.
I don't know what street Priyesh lives on.
There are no dogs allowed here.

**new:** not old **knew:** verb, past tense of know

Jafar has a new Bike.
Nilima knew where Rakhi lived.
The new theatre has comfortable seats.

**write:** verb, to make purposeful marks, for example with a pencil
**right:** to be correct or a direction opposite of left

Put your name in the upper right corner.
Please write your name on the paper.
Yes, that answer is right.

**allowed:** permitted **aloud:** out loud

We are not allowed to chew gum in school.
When you read aloud, it bothers me.
Are we allowed to bring pets to school?

**Review Work**
Underline the subject pronouns, object pronouns and possessive pronouns with red.

**Draft Book**
Choose one pair of homophones. Write two sentences with each word.

83

**RW: Underline you, I, your, your, we, you, it, me and we with red.**
**DB: Answers will vary.**

**Page 84**

Name ____________

**We Sound the Same** homophones

Homophones are words that sound alike but are spelt differently and have different meanings.
**Write the correct homophone on the line.**

**here:** location word **hear:** to understand sound by way of the ear

Did you hear the owl hooting last night?
They were here last night.
You can sit here beside me.
Sorry, I couldn't hear you.

**by:** near **buy:** to purchase

Put the pencil by the stack of books.
I would like to buy that toy.
Where can I buy new shoes?
Karuna is standing by the water fountain.

**there:** location word **their:** possessive pronoun **they're:** contraction for they are

Would you put this paper over there?
He will go there for vacation.
Do you think their mother likes snakes?
They're bringing a snake home.
I think they're still in gym.

**Review Work**
Underline the subject pronouns, object pronouns and possessive pronouns with red.

**Draft Book**
Choose one pair of homophones. Write two sentences with each word.

84

**RW: Underline you, they, you, me, I, you, I, I, you, he, you, they, I and they with red.**
**DB: Answers will vary.**

**Page 85**

Name ____________

**To, Too, Two** homophones

To, too, and two are homophones.
**to** is used in place of toward or with a verb: Rita went **to** school. I like **to** eat candy.
**two** is a number word for the numeral 2: Irfan has **two** sisters.
**too** means also or more than enough: Uday wants some milk, **too**. That music is **too** noisy.

**Write *to, too* or *two* on each line.**

tanya left at two o'clock
is that soup too hot
are you tired, too
Two lions roared
my aunt plans to come to our football game, too
you can have two stickers, too
tina went to two amusement parks this summer
anant broke two crayons
we saw two hours of fireworks
anjali threw the ball to arun
please give those two crickets to george
sheila will mail the letter to alia

**Review Work**
Add uppercase letters and ending punctuation.

**Draft Book**
Write three sentences with each meaning of these homophones.

85

**RW: Add uppercase letters and ending punctuation. DB: Answers will vary.**

**Page 86**

Name ____________

**Evening** declarative sentences

A declarative sentence tells something. It begins with an uppercase letter and ends with a full stop.
**Cross out the first letter of each sentence and write the uppercase letter next to it. Put a full stop at the end of each sentence.**

T the sky is beginning to darken .
A a shooting star streaked across the sky .
I i wonder how far away the nearest star is .
H haley looked at stars through the telescope .
D dev saw Jupiter and Venus last night .
T the stars are not as bright as the moon .
M many noises can be heard at night .
I i don't like night noises that are scary .
T the full moon is rising above the trees .
I i heard an owl hoot .
I it is time to go to bed .

**Review Work**
Circle the adjectives with orange.

**Draft Book**
Write six interrogative and six declarative sentences. Begin each sentence with an uppercase letter and end it with the correct punctuation mark.

86

**RW: Circle shooting, nearest, bright, many, night, scary and full with orange.**
**DB: Answers will vary.**

**Page 87**

Name ____________

**I Want to Know** interrogative sentences

An interrogative sentence asks a question. It begins with an uppercase letter and ends with a question mark.
**Rewrite each interrogative sentence. Put an uppercase letter at the beginning and a question mark at the end.**

who owns that red bike
Who owns that red bike?
what kind of insect is that
What kind of insect is that?
how did the kite get stuck in that tree
How did the kite get stuck in that tree?
where do fruit bats sleep
Where do fruit bats sleep?
who was emperor Ashoka
Who was emperor Ashoka?
did it rain in Bangalore
Did it rain in Bangalore?
will you turn off that loud music
Will you turn off that loud music?
are those cookies still hot
Are those cookies still hot?

**Review Work**
Some of the sentences above have linking or helping verbs. Underline these verbs with blue.

**Draft Book**
Write five interrogative sentences. Begin each sentence with an uppercase letter and end it with a question mark.

87

**Page 87 (cont.)**

**RW: Underline is, did, do, do, will and are with blue. DB: Answers will vary.**

**Page 88**

Name ____________

**Where?** declarative and interrogative sentences

A declarative sentence tells something and ends with a full stop. An interrogative sentence asks a question and ends with a question mark.
**Put the correct punctuation mark at the end of each sentence. Answer the question with a declarative sentence using the information given.**

Kangaroos live where koalas live . Koalas live in Australia .
Where do kangaroos live ?
Kangaroos live in Australia.

Wild penguins do not live north of the equator . Alaska is north of the equator .
Do wild penguins live in Alaska ?
Wild penguins do not live in Alaska.

Monarch butterflies migrate to Michigan in the spring . These butterflies migrate to Mexico in the fall . Are monarchs in Michigan in winter ?
Monarchs are not in Michigan in winter.

Orangutans live in a small part of Southeast Asia . The Brazilian rain forest is in South America . Do orangutans live in the Brazilian rain forest ?
Orangutans do not live in the Brazilian rain forest.

**Review Work**
Choose one declarative sentence from each group of sentences. Underline the complete subject once. Underline the complete predicate twice.

**Draft Book**
Write your own set of interrogative and declarative sentences. Begin each sentence with an uppercase letter and end it with the correct punctuation mark.

88

**RW: Answers will vary. DB: Answers will vary.**

**Page 89**

Name ____________

**Wow!** exclamatory sentences

An exclamatory sentence shows strong feelings and ends with an exclamation mark.
**Rewrite each exclamatory sentence. Put uppercase letters where they belong and exclamation marks at the ends.**

this dessert is delicious
This dessert is delicious!
that comet is breathtaking
That comet is breathtaking!
we're going to bangalore
We're going to Bangalore!
ouch, get off my foot
Ouch, get off my foot!
you startled me
You startled me!
the fireworks are incredible
The fireworks are incredible!
i did not crack that plate
I did not crack that plate!

**Review Work**
Choose one sentence from above and draw a star next to it. Pretend that sentence is the answer and write a question for it.

**Draft Book**
Write five exclamatory sentences. Begin each sentence with an uppercase letter and end it with an exclamation mark.

89

**RW: Answers will vary. DB: Answers will vary.**

**Page 90**

Name ____________

**Amusement Park** declarative, interrogative and exclamatory sentences

A declarative sentence tells something and ends with a full stop. An interrogative sentence asks a question and ends with a question mark. An exclamatory sentence shows strong feelings and ends with an exclamation mark.
**Put the correct punctuation mark at the end of each sentence. Write *declarative, interrogative* or *exclamatory* on the line.**

our class is going to the amusement park . declarative
the bus will leave early . declarative
did you set your alarm clock ? interrogative
abu and i stood in line together . declarative
yikes, the food here is expensive ! exclamatory
did you bring lunch ? interrogative
i'm glad i did . declarative
we put our lunches into lockers . declarative
let's go to the rides ! exclamatory
mona, julie, manas and i get in line for a roller coaster . declarative
we put on our seat belts and harnesses . declarative
i'm scared ! exclamatory

**Review Work**
Review the sentence for words that should start with uppercase letters. Cross out the lowercase letters and write the uppercase letters above them.

**Draft Book**
Write three declarative, three interrogative and three exclamatory sentences. Begin each sentence with an uppercase letter and end it with the correct punctuation mark.

90

Answer Key

Page 90 (cont.)

RW: Add uppercase letters.

DB: Answers will vary.

Page 91

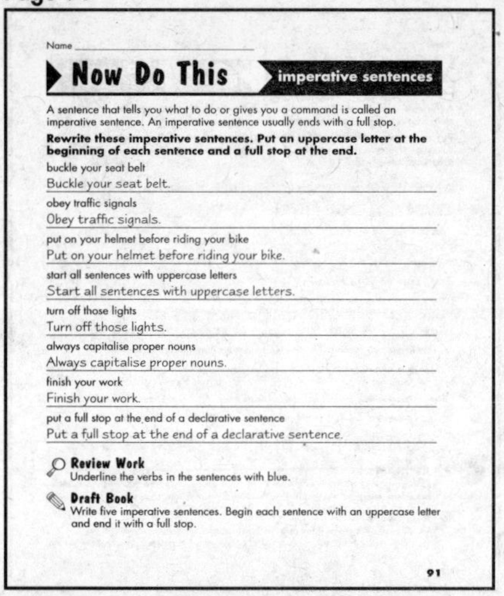
Name

**Now Do This** imperative sentences

A sentence that tells you what to do or gives you a command is called an imperative sentence. An imperative sentence usually ends with a full stop.

**Rewrite these imperative sentences. Put an uppercase letter at the beginning of each sentence and a full stop at the end.**

buckle your seat belt
Buckle your seat belt.

obey traffic signals
Obey traffic signals.

put on your helmet before riding your bike
Put on your helmet before riding your bike.

start all sentences with uppercase letters
Start all sentences with uppercase letters.

turn off those lights
Turn off those lights.

always capitalise proper nouns
Always capitalise proper nouns.

finish your work
Finish your work.

put a full stop at the end of a declarative sentence
Put a full stop at the end of a declarative sentence.

**Review Work** Underline the verbs in the sentences with blue.

**Draft Book** Write five imperative sentences. Begin each sentence with an uppercase letter and end it with a full stop.

91

RW: Underline buckle, obey, put, start, turn, capitalise, finish and put with blue.

DB: Answers will vary.

Page 92

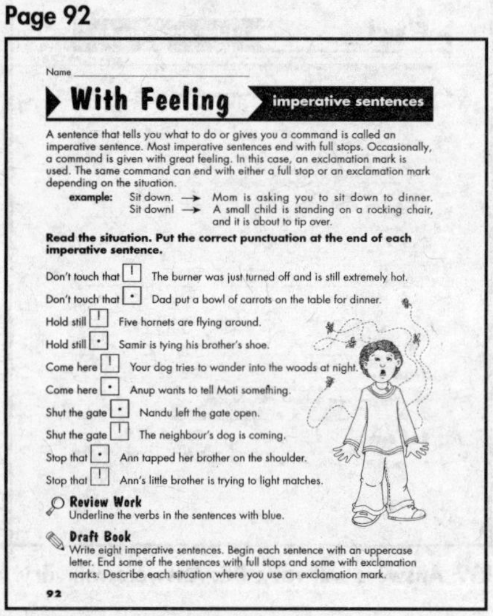
Name

**With Feeling** imperative sentences

A sentence that tells you what to do or gives you a command is called an imperative sentence. Most imperative sentences end with full stops. Occasionally, a command is given with great feeling. In this case, an exclamation mark is used. The same command can end with either a full stop or an exclamation mark depending on the situation.

example: Sit down. → Mom is asking you to sit down to dinner.
Sit down! → A small child is standing on a rocking chair, and it is about to tip over.

**Read the situation. Put the correct punctuation at the end of each imperative sentence.**

Don't touch that ! The burner was just turned off and is still extremely hot.
Don't touch that . Dad put a bowl of carrots on the table for dinner.
Hold still ! Five hornets are flying around.
Hold still . Samir is tying his brother's shoe.
Come here ! Your dog tries to wander into the woods at night.
Come here . Anup wants to tell Moti something.
Shut the gate . Nandu left the gate open.
Shut the gate ! The neighbour's dog is coming.
Stop that . Ann tapped her brother on the shoulder.
Stop that ! Ann's little brother is trying to light matches.

**Review Work** Underline the verbs in the sentences with blue.

**Draft Book** Write eight imperative sentences. Begin each sentence with an uppercase letter. End some of the sentences with full stops and some with exclamation marks. Describe each situation where you use an exclamation mark.

92

RW: Underline do touch, was turned, is, do touch, put, hold, are flying, hold, is tying, come, tries, come, wants, shut, left, shut, is coming, stop, tapped, stop and is trying.

DB: Answers will vary.

Page 93

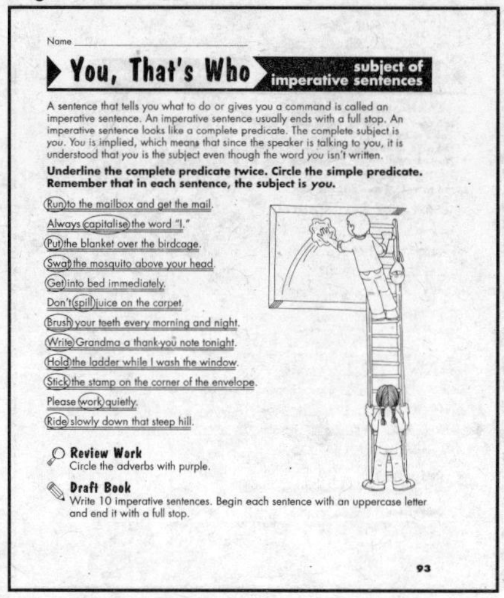
Name

**You, That's Who** subject of imperative sentences

A sentence that tells you what to do or gives you a command is called an imperative sentence. An imperative sentence usually ends with a full stop. An imperative sentence looks like a complete predicate. The complete subject is you. You is implied, which means that since the speaker is talking to you, it is understood that you is the subject even though the word you isn't written.

**Underline the complete predicate twice. Circle the simple predicate. Remember that in each sentence, the subject is you.**

Run to the mailbox and get the mail.
Always capitalise the word "I."
Put the blanket over the birdcage.
Swat the mosquito above your head.
Get into bed immediately.
Don't spill juice on the carpet.
Brush your teeth every morning and night.
Write Grandma a thank-you note tonight.
Hold the ladder while I wash the window.
Stick the stamp on the corner of the envelope.
Please work quietly.
Ride slowly down that steep hill.

**Review Work** Circle the adverbs with purple.

**Draft Book** Write 10 imperative sentences. Begin each sentence with an uppercase letter and end it with a full stop.

93

RW: Circle always, immediately, morning, night, tonight, quietly and slowly with purple.

DB: Answers will vary.

Page 94

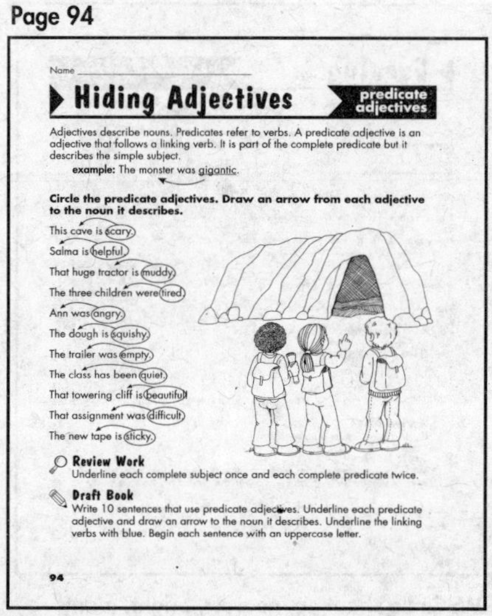
Name

**Hiding Adjectives** predicate adjectives

Adjectives describe nouns. Predicates refer to verbs. A predicate adjective is an adjective that follows a linking verb. It is part of the complete predicate but it describes the simple subject.

example: The monster was gigantic.

**Circle the predicate adjectives. Draw an arrow from each adjective to the noun it describes.**

This cave is scary.
Salma is helpful.
That huge tractor is muddy.
The three children were tired.
Ann was angry.
The dough is squishy.
The trailer was empty.
The class has been quiet.
That towering cliff is beautiful.
That assignment was difficult.
The new tape is sticky.

**Review Work** Underline each complete subject once and each complete predicate twice.

**Draft Book** Write 10 sentences that use predicate adjectives. Underline each predicate adjective and draw an arrow to the noun it describes. Underline the linking verbs with blue. Begin each sentence with an uppercase letter.

94

RW: Underline this cave, Salma, that huge tractor, the three children, Ann, the dough, the trailer, the class, that towering cliff, that assignment and the new tape once. Underline is scary, is helpful, is muddy, were tired, was angry, is squishy, was empty, has been quiet, is beautiful, was difficult and is sticky twice.

DB: Answers will vary.

Page 95

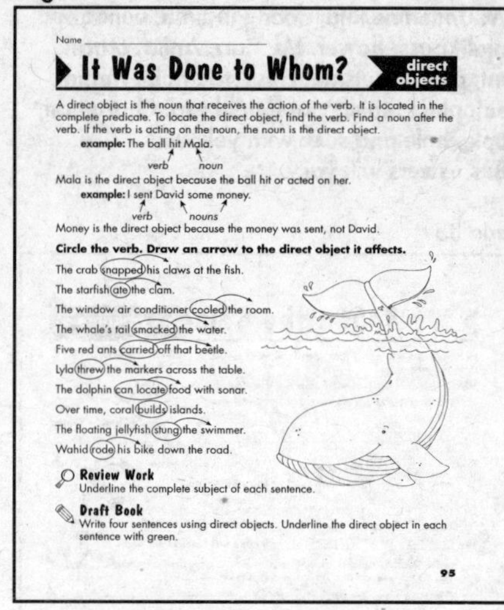
Name

**It Was Done to Whom?** direct objects

A direct object is the noun that receives the action of the verb. It is located in the complete predicate. To locate the direct object, find the verb. Find a noun after the verb. If the verb is acting on the noun, the noun is the direct object.

example: The ball hit Mala. (verb, noun)

Mala is the direct object because the ball hit or acted on her.

example: I sent David some money. (verb, nouns)

Money is the direct object because the money was sent, not David.

**Circle the verb. Draw an arrow to the direct object it affects.**

The crab snapped his claws at the fish.
The starfish ate the clam.
The window air conditioner cooled the room.
The whale's tail smacked the water.
Five red ants carried off that beetle.
Lyla threw the markers across the table.
The dolphin can locate food with sonar.
Over time, coral builds islands.
The floating jellyfish stung the swimmer.
Wahid rode his bike down the road.

**Review Work** Underline the complete subject of each sentence.

**Draft Book** Write four sentences using direct objects. Underline the direct object in each sentence with green.

95

RW: Underline the crab, the starfish, the window air conditioner, the whale's tail, five red ants, Lyla, the dolphin, coral, the floating jellyfish and Wahid.  DB: Answers will vary.

Page 96

Name

**Just a Piece** phrases and clauses

A phrase is a group of words that does not have a subject and predicate. A clause is a group of words with a subject and a predicate. An independent clause can stand alone as a sentence. A dependent clause cannot stand alone as a sentence.

**Write P if the group of words is a phrase. Write IC if the group of words is an independent clause. Add uppercase letters and punctuation, if needed. Write DC if the group of words is a dependent clause.**

IC Uday has the flu
DC whenever you can
P the enormous cookie
IC the snake coiled around the stick
P back and forth
DC because Jafar is helpful
IC Tara will baby-sit them tonight
P orange, red and yellow
P in the large jar
DC after the rain stops
P by the bushes
P sticking to the wall
P soft, velvety fur

**Review Work** Underline the nouns with yellow and the verbs with blue.

**Draft Book** Use the phrases and dependent clauses to write complete sentences.

96

RW: Underline Uday, flu, cookie, snake, stick, Jafar, Tara, jar, rain, bushes, wall and fur with yellow. Underline has, can, coiled, is, will baby-sit and sticking with blue.

DB: Answers will vary.

Page 97

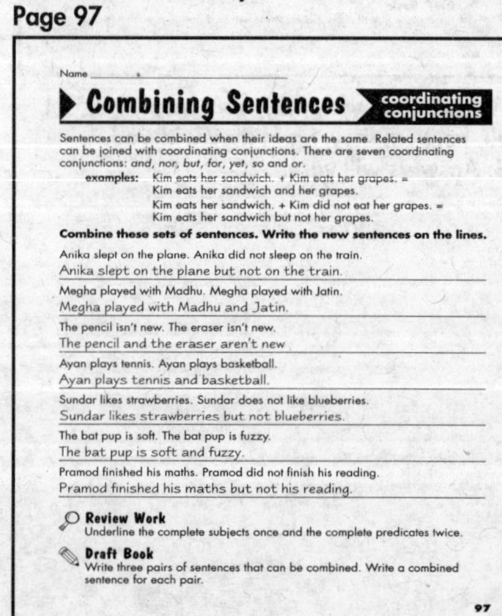
Name

**Combining Sentences** coordinating conjunctions

Sentences can be combined when their ideas are the same. Related sentences can be joined with coordinating conjunctions. There are seven coordinating conjunctions: *and, nor, but, for, yet, so* and *or*.

examples: Kim eats her sandwich. + Kim eats her grapes. = Kim eats her sandwich and her grapes.
Kim eats her sandwich. + Kim did not eat her grapes. = Kim eats her sandwich but not her grapes.

**Combine these sets of sentences. Write the new sentences on the lines.**

Anika slept on the plane. Anika did not sleep on the train.
Anika slept on the plane but not on the train.

Megha played with Madhu. Megha played with Jatin.
Megha played with Madhu and Jatin.

The pencil isn't new. The eraser isn't new.
The pencil and the eraser aren't new

Ayan plays tennis. Ayan plays basketball.
Ayan plays tennis and basketball.

Sundar likes strawberries. Sundar does not like blueberries.
Sundar likes strawberries but not blueberries.

The bat pup is soft. The bat pup is fuzzy.
The bat pup is soft and fuzzy.

Pramod finished his maths. Pramod did not finish his reading.
Pramod finished his maths but not his reading.

**Review Work** Underline the complete subjects once and the complete predicates twice.

**Draft Book** Write three pairs of sentences that can be combined. Write a combined sentence for each pair.

97

**Page 97 (cont.)**

RW: Underline Anika, Megha, the pencil and the eraser, Ayan, Sundar, the bat pup and Pramod once. Underline slept on the plane but not on the train, played with Madhu and Jatin, aren't new, plays tennis and basketball, likes strawberries but not blueberries, is soft and fuzzy, and finished his maths but not his reading twice. DB: Answers will vary.

**Page 98**

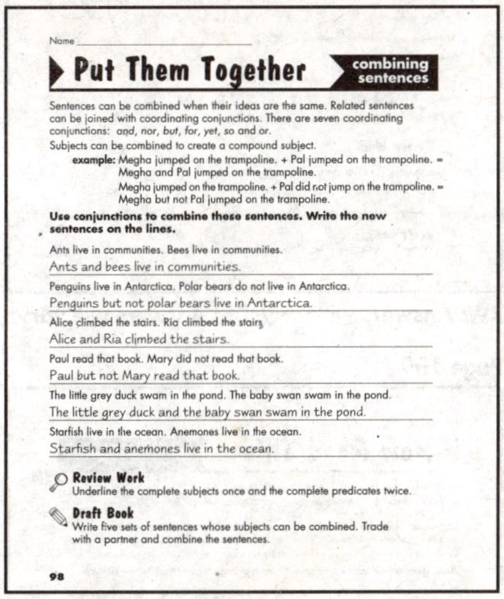

Name ____________

**Put Them Together** — combining sentences

Sentences can be combined when their ideas are the same. Related sentences can be joined with coordinating conjunctions. There are seven coordinating conjunctions: *and, nor, but, for, yet, so* and *or*.

Subjects can be combined to create a compound subject.

**example:** Megha jumped on the trampoline. + Pal jumped on the trampoline. = Megha and Pal jumped on the trampoline.
Megha jumped on the trampoline. + Pal did not jump on the trampoline. = Megha but not Pal jumped on the trampoline.

**Use conjunctions to combine these sentences. Write the new sentences on the lines.**

Ants live in communities. Bees live in communities.
Ants and bees live in communities.

Penguins live in Antarctica. Polar bears do not live in Antarctica.
Penguins but not polar bears live in Antarctica.

Alice climbed the stairs. Ria climbed the stairs.
Alice and Ria climbed the stairs.

Paul read that book. Mary did not read that book.
Paul but not Mary read that book.

The little grey duck swam in the pond. The baby swan swam in the pond.
The little grey duck and the baby swan swam in the pond.

Starfish live in the ocean. Anemones live in the ocean.
Starfish and anemones live in the ocean.

**Review Work**
Underline the complete subjects once and the complete predicates twice.

**Draft Book**
Write five sets of sentences whose subjects can be combined. Trade with a partner and combine the sentences.

98

RW: Underline ants and bees, penguins but not polar bears, Alice and Ria, Paul but not Mary, the little grey duck and the baby swan, and starfish and anemones once. Underline live in communities, live in Antarctica, climbed the stairs, read that book, swam in the pond and live in the ocean twice. DB: Answers will vary.

**Page 99**

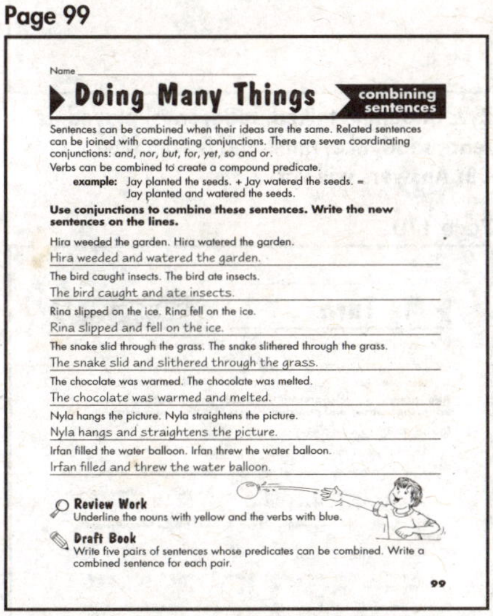

Name ____________

**Doing Many Things** — combining sentences

Sentences can be combined when their ideas are the same. Related sentences can be joined with coordinating conjunctions. There are seven coordinating conjunctions: *and, nor, but, for, yet, so* and *or*.

Verbs can be combined to create a compound predicate.

**example:** Jay planted the seeds. + Jay watered the seeds. = Jay planted and watered the seeds.

**Use conjunctions to combine these sentences. Write the new sentences on the lines.**

Hira weeded the garden. Hira watered the garden.
Hira weeded and watered the garden.

The bird caught insects. The bird ate insects.
The bird caught and ate insects.

Rina slipped on the ice. Rina fell on the ice.
Rina slipped and fell on the ice.

The snake slid through the grass. The snake slithered through the grass.
The snake slid and slithered through the grass.

The chocolate was warmed. The chocolate was melted.
The chocolate was warmed and melted.

Nyla hangs the picture. Nyla straightens the picture.
Nyla hangs and straightens the picture.

Irfan filled the water balloon. Irfan threw the water balloon.
Irfan filled and threw the water balloon.

**Review Work**
Underline the nouns with yellow and the verbs with blue.

**Draft Book**
Write five pairs of sentences whose predicates can be combined. Write a combined sentence for each pair.

99

RW: Underline Hira, garden, bird, insects, Rina, ice, snake, grass, chocolate, Nyla, picture, Irfan and balloon with yellow. Underline weeded, watered, caught, ate, slipped, fell, slid, slithered, warmed, melted, hangs, straightens, filled and threw with blue. DB: Answers will vary.

**Page 100**

Name ____________

**And, And, And** — combining sentences

Sentences can be combined when their ideas are the same. Related sentences can be joined with coordinating conjunctions. There are seven coordinating conjunctions: *and, nor, but, for, yet, so* and *or*.

**Circle the coordinating conjunctions. If the sentence has a compound subject, write *CS*. If the sentence has a compound predicate, write *CP*. If it has both, write *B*.**

CS Joy and Smita walk in the parade.
CP Rohan grabbed and climbed the rope.
CP The monkey hit the window and pounded on the wall.
CP The thief grabbed her purse and ran for the door.
CS The carpet and the couch need cleaning.
B The ants and beetles scurried and hid.
CP Mia grabs the door and slams it.
B Candies and peanuts fell on the floor and rolled around.
CS Your bedroom and the living room are messy.
B Mala and Rita swim and dive in the lake.

**Review Work**
Underline the simple subjects with yellow and simple predicates with blue.

**Draft Book**
Write five sentences with compound subjects, compound predicates or both.

100

RW: Underline Joy, Smita, Rohan, monkey, thief, carpet, couch, ants, beetles, Mia, candies, peanuts, bedroom, living room, Mala and Rita with yellow. Underline walk, grabbed, climbed, hit, pounded, grabbed, ran, need, scurried, hid, grabs, slams, fell, rolled, are, swim and dive with blue.
DB: Answers will vary.

**Page 101**

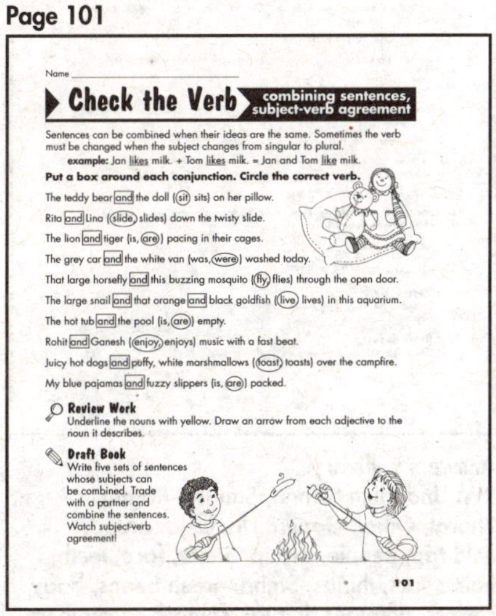

Name ____________

**Check the Verb** — combining sentences, subject-verb agreement

Sentences can be combined when their ideas are the same. Sometimes the verb must be changed when the subject changes from singular to plural.

**example:** Jan likes milk. + Tom likes milk. = Jan and Tom like milk.

**Put a box around each conjunction. Circle the correct verb.**

The teddy bear and the doll (sit, sits) on her pillow.
Rita and Lina (slide, slides) down the twisty slide.
The lion and tiger (is, are) pacing in their cages.
The grey car and the white van (was, were) washed today.
That large horsefly and this buzzing mosquito (fly, flies) through the open door.
The large snail and that orange and black goldfish (live, lives) in this aquarium.
The hot tub and the pool (is, are) empty.
Rohit and Ganesh (enjoy, enjoys) music with a fast beat.
Juicy hot dogs and puffy, white marshmallows (toast, toasts) over the campfire.
My blue pajamas and fuzzy slippers (is, are) packed.

**Review Work**
Underline the nouns with yellow. Draw an arrow from each adjective to the noun it describes.

**Draft Book**
Write five sets of sentences whose subjects can be combined. Trade with a partner and combine the sentences. Watch subject-verb agreement!

101

RW: Underline teddy bear, doll, pillow, Rita, Lina, slide, lion, tiger, cages, car, van, horsefly, mosquito, door, snail, goldfish, aquarium, hot tub, pool, Rohit, Ganesh, music, beat, hot dogs, marshmallows, campfire, pajamas and slippers with yellow. Draw arrows from twisty, their, grey, white, large, buzzing, open, large, orange, black, this, fast, juicy, puffy, white, blue and fuzzy to the nouns they modify.
DB: Answers will vary.

**Page 102**

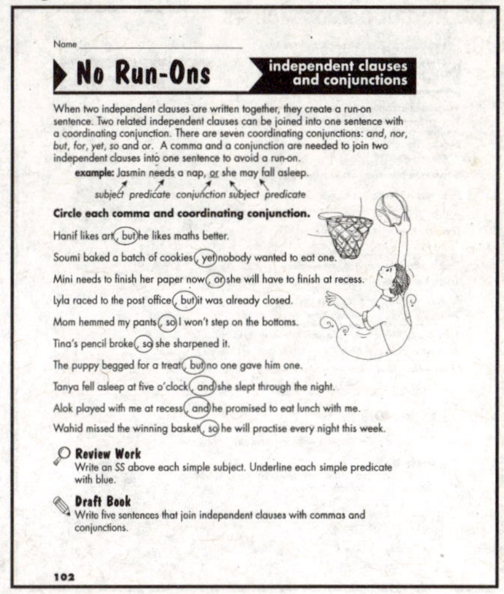

Name ____________

**No Run-Ons** — independent clauses and conjunctions

When two independent clauses are written together, they create a run-on sentence. Two related independent clauses can be joined into one sentence with a coordinating conjunction. There are seven coordinating conjunctions: *and, nor, but, for, yet, so* and *or*. A comma and a conjunction are needed to join two independent clauses into one sentence to avoid a run-on.

**example:** Jasmin needs a nap, or she may fall asleep.
*subject predicate conjunction subject predicate*

**Circle each comma and coordinating conjunction.**

Hanif likes art, but he likes maths better.
Soumi baked a batch of cookies, yet nobody wanted to eat one.
Mini needs to finish her paper now, or she will have to finish at recess.
Lyla raced to the post office, but it was already closed.
Mom hemmed my pants, so I won't step on the bottoms.
Tina's pencil broke, so she sharpened it.
The puppy begged for a treat, but no one gave him one.
Tanya fell asleep at five o'clock, and she slept through the night.
Alok played with me at recess, and he promised to eat lunch with me.
Wahid missed the winning basket, so he will practise every night this week.

**Review Work**
Write an *SS* above each simple subject. Underline each simple predicate with blue.

**Draft Book**
Write five sentences that join independent clauses with commas and conjunctions.

102

RW: Write an SS above Hanif, he, Soumi, nobody, Mini, she, Lyla, it, Mom, I, pencil, she, puppy, one, Tanya, she, Alok, he, Wahid and he. Underline likes, likes, baked, wanted, needs, will have, raced, was closed, hemmed, will step, broke, sharpened, begged, gave, fell, slept, played, promised, missed and will practise with blue. DB: Answers will vary.

**Page 103**

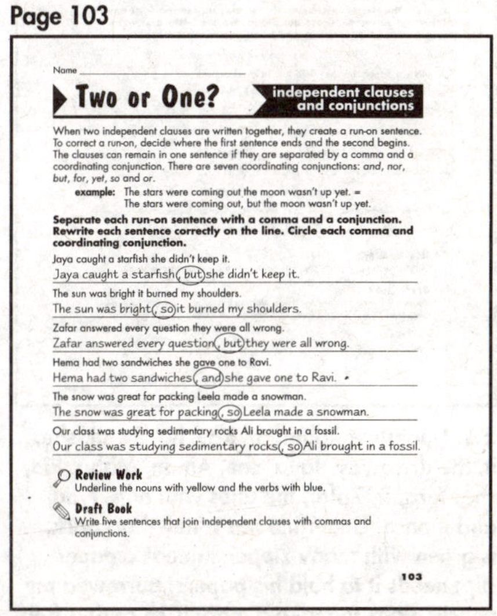

Name ____________

**Two or One?** — independent clauses and conjunctions

When two independent clauses are written together, they create a run-on sentence. To correct a run-on, decide where the first sentence ends and the second begins. The clauses can remain in one sentence if they are separated by a comma and a coordinating conjunction. There are seven coordinating conjunctions: *and, nor, but, for, yet, so* and *or*.

**example:** The stars were coming out the moon wasn't up yet. = The stars were coming out, but the moon wasn't up yet.

**Separate each run-on sentence with a comma and a conjunction. Rewrite each sentence correctly on the line. Circle each comma and coordinating conjunction.**

Jaya caught a starfish she didn't keep it.
Jaya caught a starfish, but she didn't keep it.

The sun was bright it burned my shoulders.
The sun was bright, so it burned my shoulders.

Zafar answered every question they were all wrong.
Zafar answered every question, but they were all wrong.

Hema had two sandwiches she gave one to Ravi.
Hema had two sandwiches, and she gave one to Ravi.

The snow was great for packing Leela made a snowman.
The snow was great for packing, so Leela made a snowman.

Our class was studying sedimentary rocks Ali brought in a fossil.
Our class was studying sedimentary rocks, so Ali brought in a fossil.

**Review Work**
Underline the nouns with yellow and the verbs with blue.

**Draft Book**
Write five sentences that join independent clauses with commas and conjunctions.

103

RW: Underline Jaya, starfish, sun, shoulders, Zafar, question, Hema, sandwiches, Ravi, snow, Leela, snowman, class, rocks, Ali and fossil with yellow. Underline caught, did keep, was, burned, answered, were, had, gave, was, made, was studying and brought with blue.
DB: Answers will vary.

**Page 104**

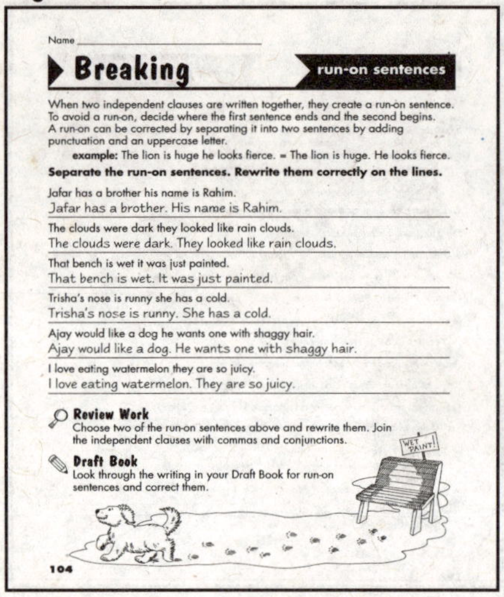

RW: Answers will vary. DB: Answers will vary.

**Page 105**

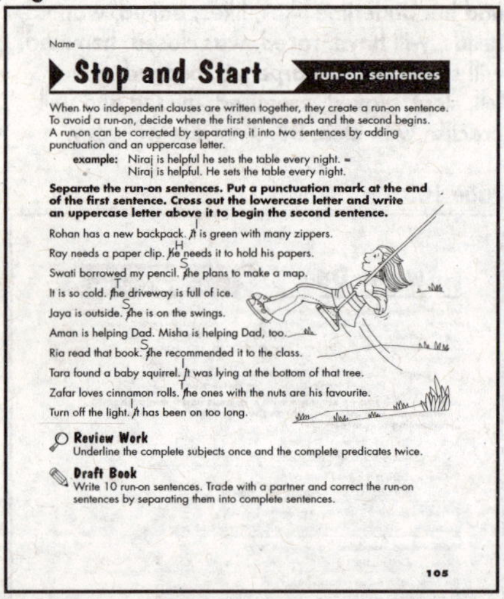

RW: Underline Rohan, it, Ray, he, Swati, she, it, the driveway, Jaya, she, Aman, Misha, Ria, she, Tara, it, Zafar, the ones with nuts, (you) and it once. Underline has a new backpack; is green with many zippers; needs a paper clip; needs it to hold his papers; borrowed my pencil; plans to make a map; is so cold; is full of ice; is outside; is on the swings; is helping Dad; is helping Dad, too; read that book; recommended it to the class; found a baby squirrel; was lying at the bottom of that tree; loves cinnamon rolls; are his favourite; turn off the light; and has been on too long twice.
DB: Answers will vary.

**Page 106**

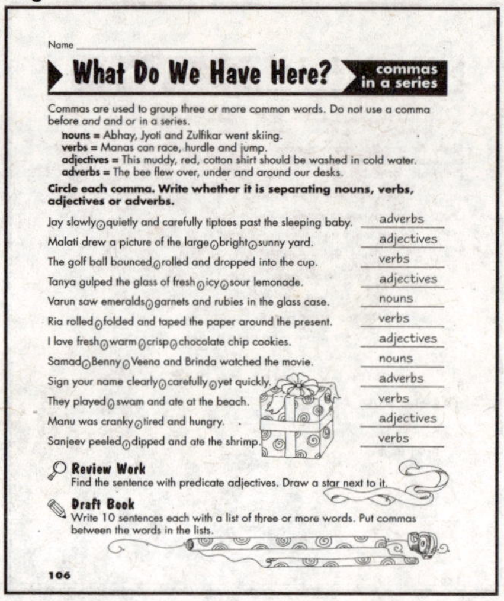

RW: Draw a star next to sentence eleven.
DB: Answers will vary.

**Page 107**

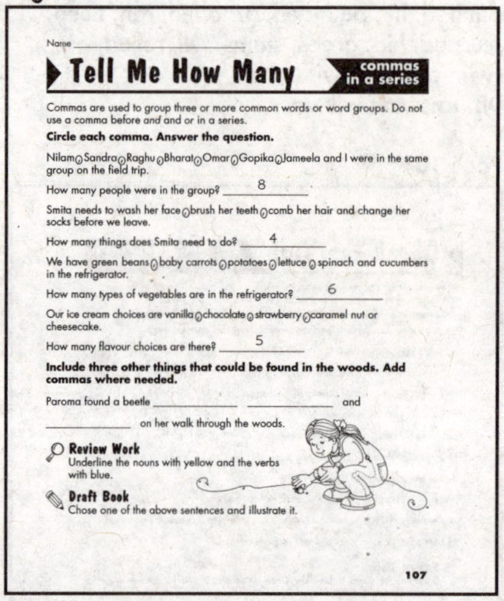

Answers will vary.
RW: Underline Nilima, Sandra, Raghu, Bharat, Omar, Gopika, Jameela, group, field trip, people, group, Smita, face, teeth, hair, socks, things, Smita, green beans, baby carrots, potatoes, lettuce, spinach, cucumbers, refrigerator, types, vegetables, refrigerator, choices and choices with yellow. Underline were, were, needs, wash, brush, comb, change, does, have, are, are and are with blue.
DB: Answers will vary.

**Page 108**

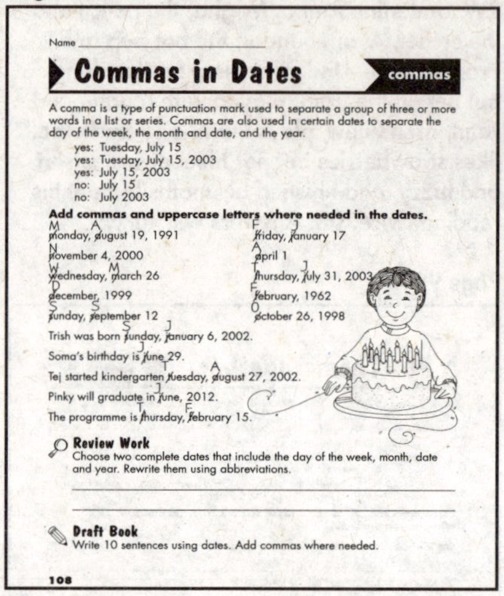

RW: Answers will vary. DB: Answers will vary.

**Page 109**

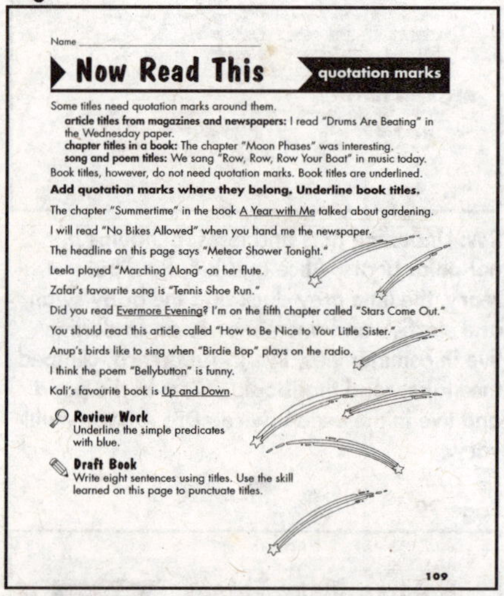

RW: Underline talked, read, says, played, is, read, read, like, think and is with blue.
DB: Answers will vary.

**Page 110**

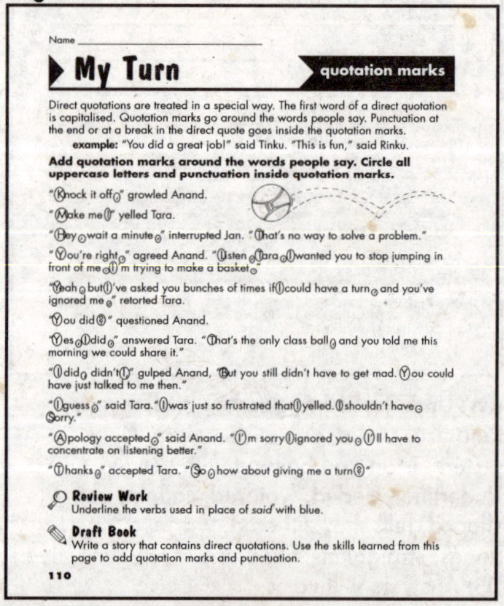

RW: Underline growled, yelled, interrupted, agreed, retorted, questioned, answered, gulped and accepted with blue.